THE INSTITUTION OF CIVIL ENGINEERS
INFRASTRUCTURE POLICY GROUP

CONGESTION

D1511592

Thomas Telford, London

Top two cover photos courtesy of The Press Association Ltd.

A CIP catalogue record for this book is available from the British Library.

Published for the Institution of Civil Engineers by Thomas Telford Ltd, Thomas Telford House, 1 Heron Quay, London, E14 9XF.

First published 1989

ISBN 0 7277 1537 2

Printed in England by Imediaprint. 1-9 Memel Street, London EC1Y OSY

CONTENTS

ANNEX

1. Introduction

1.1.   The citizen can claim that he should be able to travel freely and conveniently between home and work, and to exploit his leisure without impediment. In practice he is faced with a narrowing choice of means to do this, and with delay, discomfort and sometimes unreasonable hazard in his travel. Industry is faced with similar uncertainties which inhibit development and increase costs. The worsening of this situation will increase in pace unless immediate steps are taken. This report addresses the courses open in tackling the problem. It does not suggest that the problem of congestion can be solved, for the reasons discussed, but that the effects can be contained.

1.2.   The fragility of the present situation needs no emphasis. The transportation network is now subject to pressure which threatens to precipitate a seizure: the situation in which the centres of cities, and London in particular, become choked, and subsequently paralysed for many hours. This is not speculation. It has already happened and is likely to recur with increasing frequency.

1.3.   The nature of congestion is identified. It is a direct result of economic growth, especially in the South East, which is straining and rupturing the infrastructure inherited from a less dynamic economy. This is exemplified, *inter alia*, by the dispersal of population which in turn causes longer journeys by road and rail, not only in the South East, but in cities elsewhere. Inadequate funding of the transport infrastructure today stems from the late 1970s when economic prospects were much less promising. We are now the inheritors of an underfunded infrastructure. An increase in the rate of construction of new schemes that have already been planned will help but, taking into account present planning procedures, new schemes can take 10-15 years to implement. In contrast, the causes of congestion, particularly the growth of car ownership, are rapidly expanding. This factor determines that short term measures which can be immediately effective must attract priority. This means more effective transport management.

1.4.   This urgency is underlined not simply because of the frustration and inconvenience, but also because of the costs. Some direct costs can be estimated, but the indirect costs cannot be separated out and are probably immeasurable. The greatest costs are in the impact on economic development of the uncertainty induced by congestion, the implications of emergency situations, the increase in commuting arising from dispersal outside conurbations, damage to the City's status as an international financial centre, and diminished tourism. These have an effect beyond simple quantification, evident not only to those affected but also to the wider public. It is unlikely that the safety risks to the citizen caused by overcrowded situations will be overlooked. The issues will undoubtedly be at the forefront of the political scene, locally and centrally.

1.5.   The report which follows has been drawn up by the Infrastructure Policy Group of the ICE with the intention of identifying the objectives which should inform future transportation policy. It does not include congestion in the airways. It does not attempt to solve the problems, but sets out the considerations and makes recommendations for short and long term measures.

1.6.   In making recommendations the ICE has been able to draw upon the wide experience of civil engineers who have not only mainly provided the transportation infrastructure with which the report deals, but who are present at all levels in planning, supporting, managing and maintaining it. This makes possible a contribution on the basis of an involvement and participation in all forms of transportation which is unique. In addition the views of the ICE local associations have been sought and these are summarized in Annex E. The report is based, therefore, on a country-wide assessment of the problem.

2. Summary and recommendations

Summary

2.1. Congestion is widespread. Its effects are damaging and enormously costly. It has come about because demand for transportation has risen consistently with increased economic activity. Infrastructure provision has not matched this growth, and public spending cutbacks in the 1970s and early 1980s, coupled with the inherent slowness of the planning process (new provision frequently takes 10-15 years to complete), have seen to this. As a result, an expanding economy is wearing down an inadequate infrastructure. The situation is therefore bound to get worse, and congestion will probably increase to choke point. This is already the case at peak times in some areas. In effect congestion is now itself acting as regulator of traffic. This is wasteful, costly and damaging to growth, environment, convenience and increasingly so to public safety. It ignores the relationship between new development and the new transportation infrastructure it demands. In view of the lengthy period of time involved in the planning and construction of a new transport infrastructure there is no possibility of solving congestion. Accelerating the rate of construction of schemes which have already been planned can offer some alleviation but the most that can be expected is that congestion can be contained. This is only practicable if congestion is replaced as a regulator of traffic by some other means.

Need for co-ordination

2.2. The key requirement is the need to co-ordinate transport provision so that maximum use is made of the comparative advantages of the different transportation modes. The motorcar will continue to be the dominant form of personal transport, but the need for co-ordination recognizes that in urban areas it is essential to co-ordinate provision with other modes of transport. The absence of this leads to the introduction of unregulated and costly measures which can be self-defeating.

2.3. Co-ordination does not mean that a cumbersome national transport plan has to be drawn up (5.29). The organizational changes required are minimal but the role of the Department of Transport (DTp) is crucial. At the national level a transport co-ordinating group dealing with all modes of transport should be established which would report directly to the Secretary of State within the framework of the DTp (5.30). A majority of the membership of the group should be users, as distinct from providers, of transport. At regional level there should be regional transportation committees (RTCs) reporting to the national committee (5.31), chaired by regional directors of the DTp and charged with the co-ordination of all modes of transport within the region. A separate RTC with some executive powers is proposed for London, on which London Regional Transport (LRT) should be represented. The formation of this RTC would recognize the special problems of London where the need for co-ordination is absolutely essential (5.35). Just as important as transport co-ordination is the need to co-ordinate overall transport provision positively with land use policies so that major new developments are adequately considered by transport plans (5.25) with the wider use of development gain in their financing.

2.4.   There are longer term measures but the vulnerability of the present situation requires immediate action to contain congestion as far as possible. Measures which have an immediate effect must attract the greatest priority in the short term.

Modifying demand

2.5.   On both road and rail, present patterns of demand generate congestion by concentrating usage in peak periods. Steps recommended to alleviate these pressures are to

(a)   encourage the use of flexi-time working (5.36)
(b)   encourage the staggering of school hours and holidays (5.37, 5.38)
(c)   encourage four day weeks for same hours (5.38)
(d)   replace national bank holidays by local holidays (after the Scottish practice) (5.38)
(e)   establish work centres in residential areas, working from home, and the integration of residential and business development (5.36)
(f)   encourage out of hours retail deliveries (5.36)
(g)   boost differential between peak and off-peak fares (5.57).

Making the most of existing roads

2.6.   The key requirement for road transport is to obtain more efficient utilization of existing road networks to provide more capacity when and where it is most needed, coupled with measures to restrain traffic. Supply and demand must be brought into better balance. To achieve this end the report proposes

(a)   the wider use of traffic management techniques (5.75)
(b)   improving enforcement of control of illegal parking and illegal loading and unloading (5.43a). The role of local authorities' responsibility for enforcement of non-moving traffic offences should be considered (5.45a)
(c)   conducting road repairs out of peak hours (5.43c)
(d)   reducing need for road repairs through improvement in the quality of road construction (whole life costing, 5.44b)
(e)   improving control over road openings by statutory undertakers (5.44a)
(f)   requiring urban constructors to limit traffic disturbances by the use, for example, of trenchless technology (5.44a)
(g)   committing resources to enable rapid response to accidents or breakdowns in signalling systems (5.44c)
(h)   the selective provision of additional road capacity (5.90).

Modifying road usage

2.7.   Balancing these supply measures are proposals to modify the volume and pattern of road usage. Key proposals are to

(a)   shift demand from private to public transport (5.26)
(b)   consider road pricing (5.19)
(c)   restrict central parking (5.45a), implement park-and-ride systems (5.80) and encourage provision of parkway stations (5.54)
(d)   tighten enforcement of parking regulations and traffic law (5.45e)
(e)   introduce traffic calming measures in residential areas (5.45d)
(f)   introduce pedestrianization in urban centres (5.78).

Motorways and trunk roads

2.8.   Recommendations specifically intended to ease congestion on inter-urban motorways and trunk roads are

(a)   crawler lanes for HGVs (5.87)
(b)   more lanes at junctions to facilitate acceleration and deceleration (5.88)

(c)   introduction of ramp metering (junction control) (5.88)

(d)   improvements in the quality of road signs and better visual warning of hazards (5.89)

(e)   better management of lane closures with use of low traffic flow periods (5.89)

(f)   strengthening of hard shoulders (5.89).

2.9   Additional provision is recommended for new motorway infrastructure to serve east coast ports (including the East Coast Motorway) (5.118a).

Public Transport
Bus

2.10.   More journeys than before will need to be undertaken on public transport. In the short term buses are the only transport mode capable of rapid expansion. To further bus usage it is recommended to (5.61)

(a)   increase frequency

(b)   introduce bus stops with lead-time indicators

(c)   introduce travel card only buses on key routes

(d)   introduce collective taxis on scheduled routes

(e)   improve off-peak service to support existing flexible working

(f)   review of bus deregulation (5.64) with the scope for small buses being assessed (5.63).

Rail

2.11.   In the short term rail usage should be encouraged by increasing train length and frequency of service on British Rail (BR) (5.48) and offering tax concessions on the purchase of season tickets (5.9). On inter-city and provincial routes rail passenger congestion should be eased by delaying retirement of, and building new rolling stock (5.103) and increasing line capacity in urban areas.

2.12.   The Channel Tunnel opens up major opportunities for rail freight. To ensure that the rail network remains reasonably uncongested steps should be taken to ensure that all aspects of rail freight capacity remain adequate to meet growth in effective demand, including a freight network extending past London to the North (5.117a).

2.13.   For some large urban areas it may be appropriate to introduce light rail transport systems (LRT) (5.76), with pedestrianization in central urban areas (5.78).

London

2.14.   London is very much a special case where congestion is concerned. Acknowledging this, the recommendations specific to the capital are the

(a)   construction of new infrastructure to relieve M25 congestion (5.118b)

(b)   implementation of cross-rail proposals in Central London Rail Study (5.49)

(c)   provision of additional high capacity rail links to Docklands area (5.60) and new links to south-west and south-east London (with consideration given to provision of LRT systems in suburban areas) (5.54).

2.15.   Government assistance with the financing of this infrastructure will be essential. Additional financial provision should be sought from developers and other parties who would gain from provision of better transport linkages.

2.16. Scope for new road construction in London is limited and Government should consider the introduction of road pricing (5.45b-c) in addition to the traffic limitation measures outlined above (2.6).

Role of Government

2.17. Although the provision of a new transport infrastructure will take several years, to make sure that future provision is adequate and does not repeat the errors of the past, the Government should take immediate steps to improve forecasting methods and take account of generated traffic (Chapter 4). In the longer term there needs to be a reform of public inquiry procedures to obtain earlier decisions (Chapter 4) and to provide better and more flexible means of compensation to reduce long term costs, with the introduction of a common basis for investment appraisal across all modes of transport (5.12).

Financing

2.18. Although the Government should continue to provide the bulk of the necessary funds, to assist the big increase in investment, access to non-governmental funding sources should be maximized with current restrictions being eased. This entails the need for the following changes.

(a) European Community (5.16b). Additionality restraints on use of EC grants by local authorities should be eliminated.

(b) Private sector (5.14). Private funding will never replace the dominant role of governments in providing transportation infrastructure, but for certain projects the entrepreneurial skills and capital of the private sector can be an important condition for success. With the retirement of the Ryrie Rules there is a need for the Government to specify as clearly as possible the criteria which regulate private investment in infrastructure projects (5.15).

(c) Non-paying beneficiaries (5.53). Measures including infrastructure taxes should be considered to recover some of the unpaid benefits from transportation improvements, for example from adjacent land owners or developers. Procedures available to local authorities to obtain funds from developers for specific infrastructure improvements (Section 52 of the Town and Country Planning Act 1971) should be enhanced.

3. Congestion - definition and consequences

Introduction

3.1.   The demand for transport has been rising steadily for over 30 years.   The development of transportation infrastructure has not matched the increase in demand. Congestion is increasing throughout most of the major population centres of Great Britain and is becoming critical in some of the large conurbations.   It is increasing on motorways, trunk roads and other primary routes and even in the smaller towns and rural areas. Congestion is not just confined to the road system; it is a serious problem on inter-city and suburban rail, the London underground and other parts of the transport system.

3.2.   It is likely that in the 1990s congestion will worsen substantially and there is a danger that major damage to industry and commerce will result. A major public backlash must be expected.

Definition of congestion

3.3.   Congestion arises because more people wish to travel at a given time than the transportation system can accommodate: a simple case of demand exceeding supply. For an ordinary commodity this would be brought into balance with supply by the adjustment of the price. In the case of roads the price of access is nil whether the roads are heavily congested or empty. The only force acting to bring demand in line with supply is the level to which travellers will tolerate delay. Where it is allowed to occur, congestion becomes the primary mechanism for the management of the road network on a day to day basis and chronic overcrowding has a similar impact on rail based systems. This is the present situation.

Impact

3.4.   The impact of congestion leads to a range of problems.

(a)   Delays and unreliability. Congestion causes delays but because the delays are unpredictable additional time must be allowed for the completion of all journeys. Unreliability caused by congestion is a major problem for the public and industry.

(b)   Loss of efficiency. Congestion reduces the output of a transportation system, leaving it less able to deal with the increased numbers. As congestion increases, output decreases. In the short term congestion is not self-regulatory but self-aggravating. Once congestion is endemic in a transport system, random events such as accidents, breakdowns or repairs cause paralysis.

(c)   Massive costs.   The costs of congestion in wasted resources are enormous. Some estimates have valued these at many billions of pounds per annum.

(d)   Loss of comfort and environmental damage. Overcrowding results in loss of comfort and the environment is disrupted by pollution, noise and visual intrusion.

(e)   Reduced safety.   On public transport, overcrowding increases evacuation times and exposes passengers to greater risk of injury; response time by emergency services is greatly increased as congestion impedes rescue service.

(f)   Restriction of growth.   Congestion, by impeding access of employees and increasing distribution costs of firms, can restrict growth.

Congestion – now and the future

3.5. Traffic jams are the most obvious symptom of congestion on the roads and are perceived by the public as the principal indicator of congestion. Traffic jams first appear when temporary reductions in supply of road space are caused by accidents or road works which coincide with peak demand. The jam resolves as soon as demand subsides. As the level of traffic increases, peak periods of demand spread throughout the working day. Random events begin to have a greater effect. Ultimately the level of traffic increases to an extent that the system is operating to full capacity throughout the working day and at that point even minor disruptions throw the whole system into chaos.

3.6. Congestion may jeopardize the future of the City as a leading international financial capital. The forecasts for the growth in employment in central London and Docklands are between 200,000 and 300,000 by the year 2001, representing an additional 27% increase in peak period commuters.

3.7. Use of sections of the M25 is known to exceed greatly their design capacities and on top of the local increase in traffic the Channel Tunnel may add a further 20% to existing traffic levels.

3.8. Many portions of the inter-urban motorway network are suffering from congestion. The DTp in 1986 stated that 20% of the motorway network was overloaded. Since that date the level of traffic has increased by 36%. There is the real danger that regions of the United Kingdom outside the South East will be cut off from access to the markets of Europe by congestion in the motorway network and in the South East.

3.9. There are two aspects of congestion which need to be considered, namely

(a) public perceptions
(b) technical and economic definitions in quantitative terms.

Extent and definition

3.10. There is no nationally assembled set of definitions of what constitutes congestion. Users put up with levels of congestion in parts of our transportation systems which they would condemn as wholly unacceptable in other parts.

3.11. Congestion is a symptom, not a cause. Congestion is a consequence of inadequate provision and/or unregulated demand. In practice, users seem to accept that what is tolerable in the excess of demand over supply is influenced by the extent of the problem and the availability of resources.

3.12. There are thresholds where users move from tolerance to a clamour for action. Intolerable congestion is now widely recognized in several modes and at many locations. This means that a number of these thresholds have been crossed.

3.13. Private users of transport systems assess the impact of congestion on their quality of life. Transportation planners, economists and business users are more directly influenced by costs and efficiency. It is the perceptions of private users, however, which appear to offer the most useful approach to the definition of thresholds of unacceptability. They perceive congestion of transport systems when

(a)   there are delays which add significant time to their reasonable expectations of how long it will take to complete their journeys
(b)   they experience an untoward degree of overcrowding and discomfort in the course of travel.

3.14. Annex A1 discusses how these perceptions may vary between the modes and sectors of transport services and suggests how they could be developed to provide the definition of unacceptable congestion. Some providers of transport services have described circumstances of this kind but there is no coherent national approach. There is clear benefit to be obtained from stating appropriate standards for each sector and it is suggested that the DTp should set about the collection and publication of data on the current position.

Consequences

3.15. Although it is impossible to put a value on all the consequences of congestion, it is possible to draw some painful conclusions about the order of magnitude in quantitative or qualitative terms of the

(a)   loss of reliability
(b)   wastage of time, increased costs and loss of efficiency
(c)   lowering of quality of life and loss of comfort
(d)   lowering of quality of environment
(e)   increased accidents
(f)   restriction of development and redevelopment potential.

Reliability

3.16. The effect of congestion causing delays is obvious and needs no explanation. However, a large proportion of journeys are made with specific deadlines: journeys to work, journeys to appointments, to meet ferries or air services, or to deliver goods just in time. When transportation systems begin to suffer from congestion, reliability is one of the first characteristics to deteriorate.

3.17 Accidents, breakdowns, illegal parking, roadworks, points and signals failures, mechanical breakdowns and so on, are facts of life in a transportation system – all are capable of causing widespread disruption. Even the effect of rain can be to reduce capacity by 14% to 19%. Unless a transportation system has the robustness to cope with these adverse conditions travel becomes unpredictable.

Costs

3.18. It is clear that there are direct costs which arise from either the impact of congestion or plans to avoid it. Both of these are real cash costs to industry, and commerce and may incur real cash costs for individual travellers, for example in extra fuel while creeping slowly forward. There are also the hidden costs of some of the other factors considered, which may not appear on balance sheets, but are met from the public purse or lost in unrecognized inefficiencies. Finally, there are the economic or opportunity costs of resources deployed on coping with congestion which would be better used in developing the economy.

3.19. An analysis of the costs of congestion is provided in Annex B2. Calculations of this kind are, of course, conjectural. Furthermore, they are assessed against the unrealistic assumption of a congestion free transport system. This is a starting point, nevertheless, for a discussion about how far a reduction should be sought in the total cost of congestion to the economy, which the analysis suggests is of the order of £10 billion per annum. It would require a capital sum of £83 billion invested at the Treasury's test discount rate of 7% to cover this cost.

Quality of life

3.20. Comfort and convenience are very influential factors in the decisions people make about their mode of travel, when they will travel and how often. Reasonable standards of comfort and convenience are perceived as proper to rail, bus and personal travel by car, for whatever purpose. Convenience also expresses a need of commercial operations. It is evident that the definition of thresholds, discussed earlier in this chapter, must take account of acceptable levels of comfort and convenience.

3.21. However, these are abstract concepts. Most people seek the enjoyment of a good standard of living or quality of life. Mobility through the ready availability of comfortable and convenient transport systems has been a growing asset of those who live in developed western societies. Congestion is not only a symptom of the desire to exploit that asset, but also a positive setback to an improving quality of life.

3.22. There is no way of measuring quality of life. Yet it is a fundamental consideration in tackling congestion, because, for many, mere containment of congestion would mean an actual loss of the quality of life that they have come to expect and wish to enjoy.

Environment

3.23. The increased use of all forms of transport may represent an enhancement of the quality of life of the users, but the urban and rural areas around the arteries of movement suffer a loss. Congestion, especially of the road system, represents a particular and localized setback to the containment of environmental impact of transport systems. Queues of slow moving vehicles concentrate air and noise pollution and add to the sense of separation in communities, divided by the congested corridor. The worse the congestion, the greater the physical impact on buildings and people and the greater the financial impact on property values and trading opportunities. Some of these impacts fall within the scope of the analysis in Annex C2.

Accidents

3.24. Accidents on the road system have been reducing but are still of sizeable concern. Many are unrelated to congestion, but congestion increases the potential for accidents. For example congestion is the direct cause of frequent shunt accidents on motorways, though motorways are much safer than other parts of the road system in relation to the volume of traffic carried. These accidents do not normally occur in uncongested conditions. The congestion which follows an accident frequently spawns further accidents.

3.25. In urban areas, congestion increases accident risks for pedestrians and cyclists. Lower speeds diminish severity, but congestion increases frequency. All traffic accidents incur direct costs for the people involved – loss of wages, payment for repairs, legal fees and compensation to others. Insurance only spreads the burden. These costs can be assessed and are included in the analysis in Annex C2. Other costs, such as pain, disablement and disruption of normal life can be expressed only partly in financial terms.

3.26. Congestion increases the risk of accidents in public transport systems, especially on railway platforms and in the subways and staircases connecting into underground stations. When there is a railway accident, the risk of injury is much increased by the presence of standing passengers.

Development

3.27. Where existing development has become run down, wholly or partly due to a congested transport system, the prospects of acceptable redevelopment and growth are diminished. Annex B1 discusses the relationships between congestion, land uses and planning control. It is clear that much new development does not provide adequate transportation to support the increased demand that the development will create.

3.28. Some substantial new developments, of which Canary Wharf in London's Docklands is an example, are authorized without either promoter or planning authority successfully anticipating the demands it will place on transport systems. There is some danger that neither the developer nor the planning authority is in a position to anticipate, agree on and deliver appropriate transport infrastructure improvements fully. The resultant congestion of access routes and modes may prejudice the viability of the whole development.

3.29. Growth in demand for road travel will mean that many locations on the main road system which might be described as busy but free flowing at present will gradually show the characteristics of congestion. As congestion worsens throughout the road system, users will seek ever more ingenious ways of avoiding the more congested places, and this will result in abnormal growth on roads which at present appear to be well below the congestion threshold. These are not improbable scenarios. They describe what has already happened, is happening and will increase.

3.30. Some of the growth in road transport demand will transfer to the railways. It is very likely to exacerbate existing congestion, because much of the congestion picture exhibits an excess of demand over supply in all modes in affected corridors. The London underground illustrates this well. Some 15 sections are critically congested and 25 stations are operating at or beyond their notional full capacity. The situation is so worrying that controlling access to stations to avoid overcrowding is being seriously considered. The prospects are that continuing growth in demand, especially in the City and Docklands, will extend these symptoms to other, as yet unaffected, stations.

3.31. Congestion on the railways arises principally from an insufficient supply of train space. On some radial routes, there are insufficient train paths for extra trains. Substantial investment in longer stations to accommodate longer trains is restrained only by finance, but more track to accommodate more trains is severely restrained by availability of space. Some longer trains can be operated and British Rail is in the process of improving rolling stock provision. Even so, in many corridors, where the growth trend is continuing, the prospect is of increasing overcrowding during periods of peak demand.

4. The causes of congestion

Introduction

4.1.   In the past half century ownership and use of motor vehicles, particularly private cars, has risen dramatically. Since the early 1950s travel by car and taxi has increased by almost 900%. By 1987 there were over 19 million cars and light vans licensed.

4.2.   Congestion, although most widespread on the roads, has affected all modes of transport as demand has risen rapidly in recent years. In the five years to 1987 rail travel as a whole grew by 26% and air travel by 38%. Problems have been most acute in London where commuting journeys have grown strongly in line with the vigorous recovery of the capital from the recession earlier this decade.

4.3.   Adding to the road traffic increases is the use of road freight transport. During the period 1977-87 distances travelled by road goods vehicles declined from 19.56 billion vehicle kilometres to 19.41, but thence forward increased steadily to 23.61 in 1987. This latter increase, amounting to almost 22% in the last five years, appears to be continuing.

Incomes

4.4.   The single most important economic factor influencing this pattern of demand is growth in levels of income or gross domestic product (GDP). Transport is seldom demanded for its own sake: propensity to travel is intimately linked with those goods and services which intrinsically depend upon mobility, for example travel, foreign holidays, second homes. In addition, workplaces, shops and community facilities (such as schools and hospitals) are increasingly located to encourage access and trips by private car. Consumption of all of these increases, sometimes disproportionately, with income. In the past 25 years the steady fall in the working week coupled with increases in holiday entitlement have greatly widened the access of the bulk of the population to leisure opportunities. This has encouraged travel, particularly by car.

4.5.   Car ownership and use varies by income. In 1985 98% of households in the UK with weekly incomes greater than £350 owned a motor vehicle; this compares with a figure of 23% for the poorest households (those with incomes below or equal to £40 a week).

4.6.   Thus in the UK over the past decade the growth of expenditure on passenger transport has grown in line with the growth of the personal disposable incomes (after tax) of consumers: between 1977 and 1987 both increased by 27% in real terms. Between the different modes of passenger transport there are wide variations in response to the growth of incomes. Car travel is most strongly influenced, with spending on motoring increasing by 32% in this period. Spending on rail travel, which in 1987 accounted for only about 5% of total spending on private motoring, grew by about 9%. Expenditure on bus and coach travel fell by over 10% in the same period.

4.7.   An inescapable conclusion is that as the nation's income continues to grow, ownership (and use) of motor cars will continue

Table 1. Changes in transport expenditure in the UK 1977-87

Personal disposal income per capita	+27%
Motoring	+32%
Rail	+9%
Bus/coach	-10%

Source: Transport   Statistics 1977-87

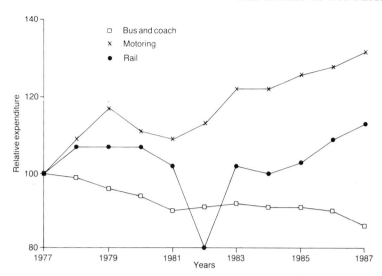

Fig. 1. Users expenditure on transportation in real terms (1977 = 100; in 1982 there was a rail strike). Source: Transport Statistics)

to grow more rapidly, eventually ceasing when the saturation level of ownership has been reached. It is also very likely that growth in rail travel, especially commuter services, will grow proportionately. That the saturation level of car ownership is still some way off is confirmed by data for motor vehicle ownership in other countries. Car ownership would have to rise by over one third to give the UK the same level of ownership as Germany.

Regional variations

4.8. Variations of growth of income and levels of income (or GDP) largely explain differences in the pattern of vehicle ownership inside the UK. Over the last decade, the biggest regional GDP growth rates, found in East Anglia, the South West and South East of England, coincided with the largest rates of growth of new motorcar ownership. Differences in the absolute level of income also correlate strongly with car ownership: in 1987 the lowest level of car ownership per capita was in Strathclyde and the highest in Hertfordshire and Berkshire.

4.9. Throughout the 1980s variations in regional growth rates have been wider than previously. This has added to the problem of congestion by sometimes concentrating growth of vehicle ownership in regions with insufficient road infrastructure to support it without congestion occurring.

Land use patterns

4.10. Transport innovations, as both railways and motorcars once were, enhance accessibility and mobility, and change land use patterns. Each new innovation in turn became the dominant mode of travel for the communities it serves. This can be seen as early as the 19th century in London and other big cities where it became possible to live much further away from the centre than previously, first with the arrival of railways and later with other forms of public transport.

4.11. The growth of motor vehicle ownership has allowed developments to be more dispersed than before, enabling people to live much further away from places where they work, shop, are educated and enjoy their leisure. Many new residential developments have been sited further and further away from traditional city centres. These residential shifts later influence the location of service industries and retail outlets. Thus there has been a tendency for longer and more frequent journeys (which are made entirely by car) to be taken. In the 20 years to 1985 average mileage per passenger journey increased by 60%.

4.12. The trip matrix – the network of typical journeys – derived from these new patterns of land use is inevitably much larger and more dispersed than before. In other words, as developments become dispersed and longer journeys are made, dependence on the motorcar is increased as it is difficult to adjust and accommodate public transport provision to these new journey networks, frequently because residential developments are too dispersed for optimal provision. In some cases the provision of public transport is ignored altogether or has been abandoned.

4.13. Land use patterns have thus changed substantially with the growth in personal mobility. Annex B1 explores these issues further and concludes that, given the key link between land use patterns and transport provision, current development control procedures are inadequate to ensure that developers provide the necessary transport infrastructure warranted by their developments.

Infrastructure provision

4.14. Capital expenditure by successive governments on transportation infrastructure has failed to keep pace with growth in demand for travel.

4.15. The prime reason for this is that attitudes of governments towards public expenditure became restrictive. This initially changed in reaction to the constraints imposed by the International Monetary Fund (IMF) in 1976-77. The IMF view, which was followed by the Government, was that public spending had to be reduced to allow more resources to be channelled into exports and investment by private companies. Later on, after 1979, public expenditure came to be seen as unwelcome in principle despite the easing of the external pressures which had precipitated the intervention of the IMF. It was argued

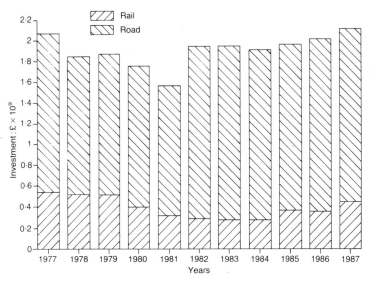

Fig. 2. Investment by Government and nationalized industries as a share of GDP. (Source: CSO)

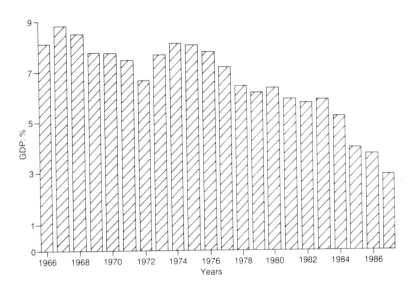

Fig. 3. Investment in road and rail (fixed assets) in real terms at 1985 prices. (Source: CSO)

that markets and not the government were most efficient at distributing resources and providing services. Thus the goal of government policy was to reduce government expenditure in real terms. Later on, when the impossibility of this became clear, the goal was modified to reduce the share of public expenditure in the national income.

4.16. Public expenditure cutbacks have had far more of a serious impact on capital spending. It is more convenient politically to cut capital programmes; and to a large extent, with upward pressure on current spending coming especially from the social security side, governments have been able to meet overall spending targets only by disproportionately cutting capital expenditure as a proportion of GDP. As a share of the nation's GDP, public investment in transport has fallen over the past decade (despite increasing as a share of total public investment). Between 1977-87 real investment expenditure in roads increased by about 9% in all. Rail investment fell by 17% in real terms in the same period. However, GDP and traffic grew by almost three times as much. This has had most serious consequences for the funding of the nation's infrastructure, contributing to congestion.

Long preparation times

4.17. Abnormally long delays (often 15 or more years) between the recognition of the need for road infrastructure and its actual provision are commonplace. The source of delay, discussed further in Annex B2, sometimes lies in the requirement for public examination and inquiry into the schemes proposed. This is necessary because major road schemes in their nature affect landowners and local residents. To satisfy democratic and political protocol and procedures their claims and rights have to be judicially compared and evaluated with those of the Government. The need to accommodate interested parties, who do not necessarily have to have a direct interest in the proposal, results in protracted hearings. Before this, there is frequently substantial delay at the initial stage between recognition of the problem and the start of detailed study of potential solutions. Delay is then further compounded by debate and indecision about the preferred solution.

4.18. Major new railway construction is relatively unusual and is secured through private bills in Parliament, a quicker process than that required for road schemes.

4.19. Even when the inquiry stage has been completed, additional delay due to alterations in Government programmes or grants can cause more delay. Throughout all these processes, bureaucratic delays are frequent.

4.20. The outcome of road schemes in the pre-implementation stage is therefore uncertain with lengthy and expensive delay being commonplace. That this need not always be the case is demonstrated by those local authority schemes where lead times have been drastically reduced by sensitive handling of pre-construction procedures and good promotion.

Problems in forecasting

4.21. Some of the assumptions in the system of forecasting used by Government to predict future traffic levels have had an adverse impact on the adequacy of some road schemes. Experience has shown that new roads have reached capacity well within their design lives and have themselves generated further traffic. The DTp has stated that forecasts for 40% of road schemes are less than satisfactory. A good example is the M25 motorway. Traffic flows on the sections of the motorway completed since 1980 are now on average over 70% above those originally forecast.

4.22. There are three main errors in forecasting procedures insofar as they relate to underprovision of roads.

(a) One of the dependent variables in traffic forecasts is national economic growth: in the past few years this has been systematically underpredicted. The Government originally assumed in the 1980s that GDP growth per capita would be in the range 0.9-1.9% per capita, but this was much smaller than the amount actually achieved (4.3% in 1987). Traffic forecasts need to include wider margins for economic and population growth.

(b) There have been significant variations between different regions of the country in economic growth. Earlier forecasting procedures did not recognize these regional variations, with the result that actual traffic flows now diverge from historical forecasts in many regions. Over the past four years these variations have ranged from 0% in London to over 20% in the east and south-east of England and in Scotland.

(c) Government traffic forecasts omit to include forecasts of generated traffic, that is journeys which are induced by the provision of new roads rather than simply transferring from other roads. The M25 is the best example of the consequences of this omission. The traffic generation effect of new roads is now well understood and could be incorporated in future forecasts.

(d) Highway schemes have been planned and constructed on the basis of inappropriate assumptions about desirable design standards. With constrained budgets, there has been a tendency to opt for the lowest acceptable design standards. These, allied to use of the low growth end of the range of traffic forecasts, have resulted in many road schemes which have been heavily loaded as soon as they are completed and congested long before the end of their theoretical design life. This has been justified with the argument that it is better to have half a road rather than none at all, but it does leads to systematic underprovision.

Political issues

4.23. Many of the solutions to road traffic congestion are either potentially extremely expensive in terms of public resources or would be unpopular with voters, especially in urban areas where the adverse effects of schemes on local communities are more concentrated and obvious and public transport alternatives more apparent.

4.24. Furthermore, there is often more political benefit to be gained in stopping or delaying major road projects than in advancing them. Environmental issues, which would not seem to be a function of car ownership, outweigh those of transport, and road transport in particular. The argument that road schemes frequently have major environmental benefits is seldom acknowledged and understood. It has also been alleged that political horizons are influenced by the proximity of the next election; this is 4-5 years at most, but with road schemes taking on average 15 years to implement it could be argued that there is more credit politically to be gained from opposing than promoting new roads.

4.25. Finally, until very recently transport as a whole was not regarded as a particularly important political issue in relation to others – such as education, the health service and housing. This perception is changing rapidly under the pressure of congestion. This calls for response from Government and the construction industry. The mechanism for dealing with transport proposals must be responsive to this need and as stressed elsewhere, co-ordination between modes of transport is essential at national and regional levels. This includes the DTp where effective co-ordination at senior level should be available. This is also true at regional level where the regional director is responsible for roads but not other forms of transport. As has been argued, the need for co-ordination of all modes both at regional and national levels is a pre-requisite for effective management of transportation.

5. The way forward

Strategic framework

5.1.   On 18 May 1989 the Secretary of State for Transport published the White Paper *Roads for prosperity* which proposes a major expansion of investment in the inter-urban road network.   The trunk road programme is to be more than doubled in size, with extensive improvements to the motorway network including the widening of the M25 and of the radial routes into London.   The improvements to the M1, A1 and M6 will do much to answer criticism that transportation links between the regions and Europe are being neglected.   Initial emphasis will be on road widening rather than the construction of new routes thereby guaranteeing faster provision because the need for public inquiry is avoided.   Coinciding with publication of the White Paper the Government released a new set of road traffic forecasts with significantly higher projections of future traffic levels.   The plans in the White Paper thus provide the hope that future road provision might be more closely matched to need, providing real benefit for road users and underpinning continuing growth in the economy.

5.2.   These proposals, however welcome, address only one part of the problem of congestion – inter-urban transport; they are concerned with only one mode of transport – roads; and they address a problem that is already here, rather than anticipating one that is about to arise. Few of the proposals announced will be completed in five if not ten years.   What is lacking from the Secretary of State's announcement is any reference to co-ordination between different forms of transport, giving support to the view that the DTp is primarily concerned with roads.   The congestion problems of inter-urban roads can indeed be largely dealt with by new construction, subject to environmental constraints.   The same cannot be said of urban congestion where the land take of new road construction is frequently unacceptable and the provision of additional road space is soon taken up by new traffic which acts to aggravate congestion in other parts of the system.

5.3.   **Developments in transport must be co-ordinated for maximum impact in tackling congestion.**   It is important that the emphasis should move away from the predominance of road investment which appears to underlie the approach of the DTp.   Co-ordination must include the relative merits of traffic management, public transport operation and investment, and demand management.   This is not a call for a national transport plan or cumbersome bureaucratic framework to regulate transport.   The necessary changes could easily be achieved within the existing framework of the DTp or could develop out of existing organizations.   **The role of the DTp in dealing with congestion as a whole must be paramount.**

5.4.   To facilitate co-ordination the following changes are required.

(a)   There should be better internal co-ordination of transportation policy in the different transport modes within DTp itself.

(b)   National and regional transport co-ordinating groups should be set up.

(c)   A separate body (a metropolitan transport authority) should be established for London.

Key issues

5.5.   Before considering the options for dealing with congestion it may be worthwhile to restate some of the most important general issues which have a particular bearing on the conclusions.

(a)   Congestion in urban areas can be contained but not cured. It may be possible to bring about improvements on inter-urban routes.

(b)   Any attempt to meet full market demand should be abandoned and resources targeted on basis of need.

(c)   Congestion should not be used as the regulator of demand for transport.

(d)   Congestion should not be used as a means to constrain development.

(e)   It is desirable to use market forces (allocation by price) to regulate transport – however when congestion arises (allocation by queue) the market becomes inefficient and must be regulated to some extent to ensure efficient operation.

(f)   The quantity and direction of capital investment in transport infrastructure must be considered.

(g)   Road traffic congestion is encouraged because road users do not have to bear all of the costs they impose on the community.

(h)   Consideration must be given to the interrelationship of transportation with land use and development density. A balance must be struck between new development and the provision of transportation infrastructure.

(i)   Because congestion and its effects vary from area to area, no single strategy will cover all its manifestations It is necessary not only to consider the various transportation modes and sectors separately but also to adopt that combination of measures which is particularly relevant to the area under consideration.

5.6.   In most cases short term measures are available, at least to contain congestion, with some longer term measures for improvement, and these are identified for each mode and sector in the proposals that follow. It must be recognized however that there is no simple remedy for congestion as widespread and diverse as the UK is now beginning to experience and the measures that are available may frequently be unpopular.

Key objectives

5.7.   **The key requirements in transport policy issuing directly from this discussion are**

(a)   **an interrelated set of policy objectives for the construction, operation and maintenance of all surface transport modes**

(b)   **a context for local authorities' decision making provided by these objectives**

(c)   **a direct reference by the objectives, *inter alia*, to urban congestion, relationship with land use policies, accessibility for all transport users and the conservation of natural resources and the environment**

(d)   **a progressive co-ordination of taxation and public finance affecting different transportation modes to provide for maximum competition (Annex C1).**

Co-ordination of transport modes

5.8.   As a result of the studies of the problems of congestion it has been apparent that it is not practicable, economical or logical to attempt to deal with the problems of congestion by dealing with each mode in isolation. Co-ordination of transportation policy implies harmonization and co-ordination of government policy in the key areas of taxation and public expenditure insofar as they affect transportation.

Fiscal neutrality

5.9. Transportation is taxed primarily as a consumption good. The present tax regime biases the consumption of transport by effectively camouflaging or suppressing the costs of motoring, thus encouraging excess demand for motoring. While there are tax concessions for the private sector there is no equivalent as regards public transport. **The introduction of tax concessions on the purchase of season tickets would go some way to redirecting the pressure away from roads.**

5.10. The tax system can be used to influence the ownership and use of motor vehicles. Proposals have been put forward to replace the road fund licence (which is a tax on vehicle ownership) by an increase in the tax on petrol (which is a tax on vehicle use). While vehicle use is the principal cause of congestion, increases in the price of petrol have comparatively little effect on distances travelled. Petrol tax increases would have to be draconian to be of any effect, and furthermore the effect would be general and not specific to those vehicles responsible for congestion.

5.11. On-street parking is increasingly a problem, narrowing the widths of residential streets and obstructing the flow of traffic and the access of the emergency services. The road fund licence might exert some control over the increase in car ownership, however more direct measures may need to be considered such as **tighter controls on residential parking to discourage a rise in the growth of ownership of motorcars which would saturate existing parking facilities and act as a source of congestion in its own right.**

Public expenditure

5.12. Different investment appraisal frameworks between modes of transport are another source of bias distorting the market for transport. Road schemes are assessed using cost-benefit analysis, rail schemes by commercial investment appraisal constrained by the need to meet criteria for the rate of return determined externally. This is unsatisfactory and imparts a permanent bias against rail investment because many of the broader benefits of rail (indeed most public transport schemes) are excluded from the investment appraisal (such as reduction in journey times and reduction of road traffic congestion). **There is a need to assess investment proposals for the various transport modes on a common basis.**

5.13. Both road and rail systems are subject to public expenditure constraints (which are determined within a decision framework in which evidence of need for expenditure is a relatively weak factor in influencing investment schemes). **Capital expenditure in transportation should be revised to relate more to need and benefit, and treated by Government on a longer term basis**, that is with a perspective not limited by annuality.

Private expenditure

5.14. Access to private capital has for many years been restricted by the operation of the Ryrie Rules. The announcement that they have been retired is welcomed. Equally welcome is the Government's decision that individual private sector road schemes should be additional to the public sector programme.

5.15. In retiring the Ryrie Rules, the Chief Secretary to the Treasury correctly said that they are thought to be incomprehensible and to hamper private finance by setting impossible hurdles. The incomprehensibility arose not from the brief and simple Ryrie Rules but from the acrescence of Treasury folklore in their interpretation and the Government's refusal to clarify its methods of assessment. The re-stated doctrine, that approval of private sector schemes is dependent on better value for money, is potentially even more prone to the same defect. The private sector can only operate effectively when the Government has stated clearly and in some detail how it will assess value for money – both generally and in specific cases. This is not a simple task but in avoiding it in the past the Government has obstructed the attainment of its own objectives.

5.16. Related measures to improve (i.e. not simply increase) the contribution of the private sector should include

(a)   extending acceptance of additionality to rail and other transport sectors

(b)   allowing recipients of EC grants and loans (including local authorities) to spend these without any offsetting reduction in UK official funding

(c)   accepting that external benefits are real for all forms of transport and can only be properly recognized by public sector contribution.

Dealing with congestion

5.17. With the above issues in mind the problems can be examined under the following broad headings with measures proposed for each sector offering the best and most practical steps for the containment or control of congestion

(a)   general measures

(b)   London – to encompass all the major transportation systems

(c)   roads – in the conurbations
        roads – inter-urban

(d)   railways – inter-urban

(e)   Channel Tunnel.

General measures

5.18. Present measures to reduce congestion are largely *ad hoc*. Solutions are commissioned for specific problems, junction improvements, bypasses, traffic management schemes and so on. Such measures can successfully hold off congestion in some urban areas and may continue to do so. However in major urban areas the scope for such measures is diminishing and the likely increase in traffic will overtake any improvements. More radical approaches are required.

Road pricing

5.19. In support of road pricing there are four fundamental points.

(a)   Very high traffic growth is a reflection of increasing social and economic activity and as such is an indicator of a thriving nation. This has led to severe congestion on all forms of transport.

(b)   Mitigation of congestion will require substantial additional physical facilities to be constructed if activities are to continue to thrive.

(c)   Physical facilities alone will be insufficient, ineffective and/or uneconomic in mitigating congestion. The time taken for construction will mean that significant relief even where available by that method will, except in very limited instances, be many years in becoming effective.

(d) Other measures are therefore required in addition to produce timely relief to congestion. The Institution believes it is now necessary to include road pricing as part of any plan to deal with London and other areas of widespread congestion.

5.20. The close relationship between rising economic prosperity and increased desire for movement has long been understood. The increase in demand provides a necessary service to continuing economic development and a contribution to the quality of life perceived by a large proportion of the population. Even at the present level of provision of facilities for movement – roads, railways and airways – increased movement only results in congestion at particular places and at particular times. Periods of congestion which are relatively brief and localized have been familiar for many years; the sensible general reaction of the public and the providers is usually that in these cases costly relief works are not justified and people can reasonably be expected to adjust their pattern of movement to cope. This applies to both public and private transport. But once congestion is long lasting and widespread the problem becomes different in kind. The uncertainty of journey time, and discomfort of travel and the sheer unavailability of service combine to make social and economic effects more damaging. This is where it becomes more practicable and economic to contemplate appropriate additional physical facilities – road and/or rail – to provide relief. Everyone will have had experience of the provision of local bypasses or motorways or new rail lines where significant and lasting relief has been obtained. It is clear that there still remain many instances where measures of that kind are likely to be sufficient in themselves to cope with present congestion and that which might reasonably be foreseen.

5.21. There are however areas and corridors of movement where the potential demand is so great that solutions relying on purely physical provision of facilities at any level which could reasonably be contemplated will be ineffective in providing for it at all times. There is also the important question of what is reasonable for the public to expect in their immediate future. It is common for individual projects to take at least ten years from conception to generation and it is certain that on physical and financial grounds, where congestion is at its worst as in London, the timescale for installing significant extra physical capacity would be substantially longer than this. So other means must be found to supplement physical measures whether those measures be rail or road based.

5.22. If present congestion is not to be tolerated and if physical measures alone are not likely to be sufficient it is necessary to contemplate measures to influence demand. There will be particular times when numbers of journeys will need to be reduced; there will be other times where no constraint is necessary. In transport systems as they operate now, public transport already influences demand at key times by the use of peak and off peak fares, whereas private and commercial transport by road has no differential constraint on it whatsoever. The time has come (if it is desired to tackle congestion where it presents the greatest difficulties, particularly in London) to introduce such differential constraints. Earlier studies have suggested that purely administrative measures to deny access to roads at peak times would be very blunt instruments, difficult to enforce and liable to have harmful economic effects. Road pricing, the charging on a differential basis at particular places and particular times for the use of scarce road space, is available and is an effective management counterpart to the possible provision of more road and railway facilities. Pricing, though new in this sphere, is a universal and sensitive means of allocation of scarce resources and there is no reason to suppose it would not be effective and acceptable once introduced.

5.23. Road pricing could be effective long before the completion of new build proposals and could alleviate congestion at an early point. Its revenues could contribute to the large cost of construction. Not the least benefit of road pricing is that this gives equality in choice in decision making by the transport user between all modes, and neutralizes the present heavy bias towards roads, which are perceived as free.

5.24. Proposals to solve congestion by massive investment have been put forward by a number of organizations. Such options carry the penalty of huge cost, both in financial and environmental terms. To attempt to match the growth in traffic by the construction of new roads would entail massive demolition of residential areas and encroachment on the countryside. It is by no means certain that the solution would be effective because experience has shown that new roads create new traffic and the effect of building roads on a vast scale might be no more than to generate traffic on an equal scale. If seeking to meet demand in this way will not work, and it appears that the opportunities for manipulating demand can be operative to only a limited extent, what options are open for the direction of resources to solve the problem?

Transport and development

5.25. The link between the development of new housing, commerce and industry, and the demand for transport is self-evident. A new cause of increased demand for transport is the dispersal of urban populations into suburban and rural areas, and the concentration of jobs in city centres. This link must be recognized and either

(a) development of new housing, industry and commerce should be balanced to levels that can be sustained by the transportation system or
(b) transportation infrastructure must be developed in parallel with new development.

5.26. In deciding priorities between modes of transportation in urban situations the balance should favour collective forms of transport rather than the individual. It needs to be recognized that improved transportation encourages development.

Market control

5.27. Using congestion as the mechanism for management and allocation defeats both economy and efficiency. Congestion results in massive loss of capacity from the transportation systems, and it allocates transport not to those who have the greatest need to travel but to those who have the greatest time to waste. Congestion may also act to prevent the growth of employment in central areas.

5.28. The problems of congestion vary from one location to another; there is no single set of solutions. It is vital however that an efficient market for transportation is created, but this will not be achieved by allowing congestion to be the regulator. The choice lies between administrative control and the price mechanism. If it is accepted that it is wrong to continue with congestion itself as a regulator because it is wasteful and inefficient, what should be put in its place? Expectations should not be aroused that there is a simple and universal solution, but it is obvious that some form of co-ordination in transport planning is required.

Organization and planning

5.29. A detailed national strategic plan for transport is unlikely to work because of the multiplicity and complexity of the factors involved and the variety of conditions in different areas. This does not mean however that there should be no attempt to monitor and control the co-ordination of transport at the national level, but the emphasis should be placed on effective structure at the regional level.

5.30. At the national level a transport co-ordinating group should be formed to advise the Secretary of State for Transport on the adequacy of the transport system in all its aspects, taking into account new developments and major investment proposals. This body should include representatives of major participants such as the Confederation of British Industry, British Rail (BR), the British Airports Authority (BAA), the Bus and Coach Council, and the Docks and Harbour Board. The Department of the Environment (DoE) and Department of Trade and Industry (DTI) should be included. The group should be chaired by a Minister or senior official from the DTp and report annually to the Secretary of State. It would deal with proposals as they arise during the year. In order that professional advice should be available, it is suggested that a member of the secretariat should be provided by the ICE with its unique access to clients, contractors, consultants, academics and local government.

5.31. At regional level there should be a body capable of monitoring transportation infrastructure across the board, involving an input into land use with a membership similar to the group. The proposal is that the DTp should provide the framework for this body based upon the regional directors (whose areas are currently linked to county boundaries) who would chair meetings on a regular basis. These RTCs could include local users, and provide a forum for consultation and support for proposals for all modes of transport within the region. Where issues involving more than one region are concerned there should be recourse to the national committee through the DTp framework. Where input from other government departments is required this should be sought by the DTp.

5.32. It is not suggested that the bodies proposed should have legislative backing, but that their status should be established by ministerial direction, making it clear that endorsement by the RTC is a necessary condition of progress for development of transportation infrastructure proposals.

5.33. Road transport in England at county level is managed by the county councils in conjunction with the DTp. There is no equivalent organization operating in major conurbations. In most cases transportation is the responsibility of a large number of independent local authorities which can be of differing political ideology, while the DTp retains responsibility for trunk roads (though not in Wales, Scotland or Northern Ireland) and motorways. Because transportation policies pursued in one borough will directly affect adjacent boroughs, it is vital that there should be some means of co-ordinating transportation policy. The RTC proposal should achieve this.

5.34. Regional organizations must be established to cover cities with the responsibility for monitoring the co-ordination of all modes of transport and with specific responsibility for co-ordinating transportation infrastructure projects mounted by adjacent local authorities. Such organizations would be well placed to ensure that development pressures and the capabilities of the transportation system are maintained in balance.

5.35. In London the establishment of a metropolitan transport authority is recommended. This should function as an RTC but should involve or be based on an expansion of LRT's role, making use of its executive powers.

Modifying demand

5.36. Pressures on overcrowded roads and transport facilities might in the longer term be eased by changes in the location of work. With electronic technology, which can be readily accessed from the home or work-centres in residential areas, regular journeys to the office may become less necessary. Home-based working offers potential scope for reducing business accommodation costs and the stress and strain of daily commuting. More modest proposals include the greater spread of flexi-time working, and the adoption of four day working, in order to spread demand both at day and weekend peaks. Both of these deserve to be actively encouraged by government. The effect of retail deliveries could be reduced by encouraging out of hours operation.

5.37. Given that congestion problems, at least in the morning peaks, are intensified by journeys to educational establishments, it should be considered whether it is feasible to stagger school hours in a particular locality so reducing journeys made at any one time.

5.38. To relieve congestion during holiday periods, it is suggested that school holidays are staggered and that the present national system of bank holidays in England is replaced by local holidays after the Scottish practice.

London

5.39. London is unique in the scale of the congestion problem and the remedial action needed to correct it. In view of the inter-relationships between the various forms of transportation, any study of congestion and improvement must consider the individual modes collectively. Any measures for improvements must be advanced in full recognition of the probable effects on other modes. **The co-ordination of transport provision, highly desirable elsewhere, is absolutely essential in London.**

5.40. Whereas Central London commuting in the morning peak has increased by some 10% in the five years to 1987, the use of private cars to commute into Central London has fallen substantially in the

Table 2.   Projections of employment growth in London 1987-2001

Area	Lower	Higher
Central London	100,000	150,000
Docklands	120,000	150,000
Total	220,000	300,000
Rest of London	60,000	120,000

Source: Transport Statistics 1977-87

Table 3.   Central London commuter traffic; peak period 1982-87

	Commuters x 10^3		Increase:
	1982	1987	%
British Rail	390	449	15
London Underground	283	403	42
Bus	99	79	-20
Private car	197	162	-18
Total	1,012	1,125	10

Source: Transport Statistics 1977-87

Table 4.   Demographic and transport predictions for the South East

	Year		Growth:
	1986	2001	%
Population			
London	6,775	6,919	2
Rest of South East	10,489	11,424	9
Traffic growth forecasts			
Long distance commuting			30-40
Morning peak central rail traffic			15

Sources: Regional Trends 1988 for population; Central London Rail Study for traffic growth forecasts same period. Overall traffic on London's roads has increased by about 1% per annum since 1976, with the bulk of this increase occurring in outer London (outside the central cordon: a radius of 2.5-3 km from Aldwych). Vehicle speeds have steadily declined at all times of the day in the central area since the mid 1970s and are now down to an average of 11.0-11.5 mph. The number of taxis in London has increased by nearly 20% over the last ten years to a total of nearly 15,000. Commuting into central London by bus has fallen by approximately 30% in the past decade whereas in London as a whole bus usage has remained broadly constant.

5.41. Since 1982 travel to Central London by BR Network SouthEast has increased throughout the period with peak arrivals up 19%. During the same period traffic on the London underground increased beyond all expectations. Usage (passenger kilometres) increased by around 70% and passenger numbers by 60%. The service operated, however, (train kilometres) increased by only 11%. Figures are not available for Docklands Light Railway which opened in August 1987, but it will be unable to cope with the traffic which will be generated by the full planned development of the Docklands.

Roads

5.42. **Shorter term options to deal with congestion on the roads are limited.** A number of traffic management systems have been introduced or are under study, such as the control systems operated by the TCSU: SCOOT (split cycle offset optimization technique) which monitors traffic to calculate optimum traffic light cycles; MOVA (microprocessor optimized vehicle automation) another and separate system still at the experimental level, which could measure incoming traffic to control it at crucial isolated junctions; and Autoguide, the electronic car navigation system which has recently been developed. Also a number of major and minor road improvement schemes are in hand or planned for the London area. There must be serious reservations about the ability of these measures to achieve lasting improvements. There is apparently a sizeable suppressed demand for car travel and it is considered that the benefits gained from any improvements will quickly be lost as further cars are attracted on to the roads. There are similar reservations about other traffic management ideas such as managing more of the main radial roads on the tidal flow principle.

5.43. **There are however a number of shorter term alternatives which offer possible advantages.**

(a) **Illegal parking or loading and unloading which restricts road widths and reduces traffic flow capacity should be vigorously tackled.** The introduction of wheel clamping has yielded positive results but a wheel clamped vehicle remains in position for a long period and continues to obstruct traffic flow. Clamping is therefore unsuited to the main radial routes. A better alternative would be to tow the vehicle away and increase both the time involved in retrieving it and the cost of doing so. The towing away operation should be put out to private enterprise to achieve the necessary rate of control.

(b) In urban areas major construction projects should be required to deliver at night or at least out of peak hours.

(c) Road repairs should be restricted to the nighttime (at least in non-residential areas) wherever possible.

27

5.44. Other measures include

(a) **the proper reinstatement of road openings by statutory undertakers.** At present statutory undertakers are required to reinstate roads to temporary standard only. The highway authority is responsible for the permanent repair. In consequence for any single road opening there are two series of road works to impede the flow of traffic. The use of trenchless technology to avoid the need for road openings should be encouraged

(b) improved quality of road construction to reduce the necessity for early maintenance. Widespread use of the system of whole life costing for road construction should be encouraged

(c) **rapid response to traffic accidents and breakdowns in control apparatus such as traffic signals.**

5.45. However, these measures would give only marginal improvements and when the forecast future traffic increases are taken into account it is apparent that longer term measures alone offer scope for significant improvement. Of these **the following are considered to offer worthwhile progress but only when combined with interrelated improvements to the public transport systems as detailed later.**

(a) **The control of trip end parking.** Single occupant car commuting is a main cause of congestion on urban radial routes. The control of trip end parking offers an effective means of regulating this traffic. This existing parking is privately controlled, parking that is within the control of the public sector should be controlled more rigorously. A role for local authorities in the enforcement of non-moving traffic offences should be considered.

(b) **The introduction of a supplementary licensing system (stickers) to control peak period traffic.** Such a system is in operation in Singapore.

(c) **The introduction of electronic road pricing.** The technology for this has already been developed, with special number plates mounted on vehicles so as to be read by roadside sensors. When a vehicle without the special plate crosses the sensor a photograph is automatically triggered. The object of introducing road pricing would be to set the cost to the road user at such a level as to materially cut traffic levels. This would not only reduce congestion but also create the free flow conditions for bus services which would enable them to offer efficient and reliable alternatives to car travel. Furthermore, it is likely that road pricing would only be generally acceptable to the public if public transport in all forms was enhanced to provide acceptable alternative travel for those who were priced off the roads. Hence the link between road pricing and the alternative use of public transport should be apparent and to this end the funds generated by road pricing should be spent directly on improvements to public transport. Furthermore the introduction of road pricing should be phased to coincide with the actual achievement of public transport improvements.

(d) In association with the introduction of road pricing, **traffic calming techniques should be introduced** wherever it proves necessary, by means of such devices as road speed humps or road narrowing to discourage rat running through unsuitable areas and speeding.

(e) **There should be penalties of greater severity for the various**

illegal driving practices such as speeding, illegal parking and so on.

5.46. There will be a considerable number of problems associated with the introduction of road pricing, such as the locations of the boundaries for the various levels of pricing, the solution to the problems raised by car parking outside the charging boundaries by motorists unwilling to pay, the treatment of residents of the areas within the charging boundaries, and the treatment of overseas visitors. All these problems are soluble with intelligent planning and the advantages offered by the system easily outweigh the costs oᵢ introducing it. It is almost unique in its ability to offer really worthwhile improvements to the lives of both the commuters to and the residents of London and can be tuned to cope with changing conditions and needs. It would result no doubt in a reduction in the road accident rates (currently nearly 50,000 per annum in London) and would also reduce pollution which is a serious problem in London.

British Rail

5.47. **The options for shorter term measures to deal with congestion on BR are more directly productive.** Pricing mechanisms could be used to reduce the number of passengers during peak hours but the effect of this would be to transfer passengers to the roads, with a resultant increase in congestion there. This underlies the need for co-ordination of modes. The only way improvement could be achieved would be the increase of capacity by BR. **BR is already taking action to increase the length of trains and platforms where practicable.** Last May for instance it added 1000 seats to some of the evening rush hour trains from Paddington although those have already been filled. In October 1988 BR was given approval to order 200 of the 300 new coaches needed to assist overcrowding. Of these, 30 four coach units are for suburban trains to King's Cross, Euston, Liverpool Street and Fenchurch Street and 20 four coach units for the new Thameslink line which opened only in May 1988 but has attracted passengers beyond all the forecasts. However, while these and similar shorter term measures will help to ease overcrowding, it is apparent that, **bearing in mind the forecast passenger increases, additional measures will be needed.**

5.48. The Central London Rail Study has now identified a number of shorter term measures designed to get the best out of the existing network, such as running additional trains, increasing train capacity and extending some platforms to accommodate twelve carriage trains. The results of all these measures might well reduce overcrowding to more tolerable levels unless the actual passenger increases exceed the forecasts.

5.49. In considering the longer term options it has been apparent for many years that the main lines serving London, which were set down in the middle of the 19th century, offer very little through London capacity and have inhibited use of the railways. **The Central London Rail Study has identified a number of cross London routes which could be of considerable value in reducing overcrowding and road congestion and the choice of the East-West Crossrail route is welcomed.**

5.50. **The nature and severity of the problems of transportation in London are such that the East-West Crossrail project must be one**

Table 5. Estimated benefit-cost ratios of new rail proposals with benefits as a proportion of total annual cost

	To public transport users	To road users	Revenue gain	Total*
Single Line Schemes				
Chelsea-Hackney	0.6	0.1	0.1	0.9
Jubilee Line				
extension to Ilford	0.4	0.1	0.1	0.6
Thameslink Metro	1.5	0.3	0.3	2.1
East-West Crossrail	1.2	0.2	0.2	1.6
North-South Crossrail	0.6	0.1	0.1	0.9
East-South Crossrail	1.4	0.3	0.3	1.4
Two Line Packages				
Full Cross	0.9	0.2	0.2	1.3
East-West Crossrail				
plus Chelsea-Hackney	0.8	0.2	0.2	1.1

* Rows may not add up due to rounding. Source: Central London Rail Study 1989

of only a number of major new investments in the transportation infrastructure.

5.51. **These schemes offer great advantages to commuters, BR and the travelling public at large and they should proceed as quickly as possible bearing in mind that even with early agreement, the first of these routes would not be in operation before 1996.** The example of similar schemes overseas, such as those in Paris, would indicate that their success is assured.

5.52. The cost-benefit analysis finds that none of the proposed links are financially viable, though most offer major economic benefits. The report states that the investment criteria imposed on BR and LRT which require investments to produce a positive financial rate of return will not be relaxed. The question follows as to how these measures, vital to the future of London, will be financed.

5.53. The cost of all the measures proposed by the Central London Rail Study for BR would exceed £2 billion and it is apparent that BR would be unable to fund such projects in addition to their planned outgoings except in the unacceptably long term. Funds could be made available by increasing commuter fares but there is always the danger of driving passengers on to the road system which is already congested to an unacceptable level. Funds may be forthcoming from road pricing but, until the public transport systems are better able to cope with the increased passenger loads on public transport, road pricing might simply add to congestion. However, a marginal reduction in traffic might make a major improvement to congestion and in these circumstances the consequences might be beneficial. As the study points out, **some of the proposed schemes would enhance land values and would, or could be made to, generate considerable financial benefits to businesses and land owners. Such beneficiaries should** therefore contribute to the cost. **The government will need to provide significant finance if these far sighted and worthwhile schemes are to proceed.** Bearing in mind that the users will be required to bear part of the costs through higher fares and that non-user benefits (such as relief of congestion on the roads) will result, there is a powerful argument for government grant.

5.54. In addition to the measures proposed in the Central London Rail Study there is a need to acknowledge the problems being encountered in suburban areas of London extending up to and beyond the M25. Here **the construction of parkway stations linking in with the motorway and trunk road infrastructure would do much to relieve peak period road congestion around stations in suburban and urban centres, and by encouraging the transfer of commuters from road to rail, would provide relief on radial roads. The scope for light rail transit systems should also be considered.**

London underground rail system

5.55. The London underground system has suffered very badly from lack of investment in the 1970s and the early part of the 1980s. The surge of new traffic, partly attributable to the introduction of the attractive Travelcard tickets, has caught the system ill prepared. (When the Travelcard was introduced to offer unlimited travel within specified areas at special rates, LRT expected to sell around 100,000 per year. Last year they sold almost 1,000,000.)

5.56. Some 15 sections of the underground are now critically congested and this will rise to more than 20 by the year 2001 if no action is taken. About 25 stations are choked, often dangerously, at peak hours, either in the ticket halls, lifts, escalators or platforms. A further 10-15 will reach the same stage by the end of the century. There is, of course, no control of the numbers boarding the trains.

5.57. The options for shorter term improvements on the London underground must include substantial fare increases for travel during the peak hours to reduce overall passenger numbers and the technology must be installed to make this effective for both morning and evening travel. This would reduce travel at the critical times and provide early relief for commuters though there would be a displacement on to other modes of travel. **The Central London Rail Study identified a number of other shorter term options. Some £450 million needs to be spent on various works at the stations suffering the worst congestion. Further spending is required to introduce additional and higher capacity trains.** However the Study does not expect such shorter term measures to eliminate overcrowding.

5.58. For longer term improvements a number of measures have already been approved, including the modernization of the Central Line, to be completed in 1996 at a cost of around £720 million. The Study has made proposals for only one new line which is that between Chelsea and Hackney at an estimated cost of £1000 million. If the two new BR Crossrail routes proceed, it is unlikely that the Chelsea - Hackney line will be approved also. However there will be further study of the possible new lines. The Paddington – Heathrow link will substantially increase the number of passengers at Paddington and in the absence of adequate interchange facilities will increase congestion there.

5.59. An equally important issue is the inadequate rail service to the new Docklands developments. The London Docklands Development Corporation estimates that the working population of the area will increase from 30,500 in 1986 to 80,000 in 1991, 165,000 in 1996 and over 200,000 by the year 2000. The Canary Wharf development will provide some 10 million square feet of office space but around 25 million square feet of office development is now committed to the Isle of Dogs and possible future developments could raise this to 30 million square feet. This is a large increase on the developments planned only four years ago and **new rail services to the area are needed as neither the Docklands Light Railway nor the local road network can be developed to cope with the expected traffic.** This demonstrates very clearly the need to link development and transportation infrastructure on a contractual basis.

5.60. Olympia and York, the developers of Canary Wharf have proposed **a new underground rail line to run 9 km from Waterloo to Greenwich with a link to the Jubilee Line at London Bridge,** all at an estimated cost of £450 million. They are willing to contribute £180 million. The East London Rail Study is looking at this proposal but **the need for the early provision of such a line is clear** and the only real issue in contention may be the amount to be contributed by the developers.

Table 6. London Dockland's employment forecasts

1986	30,500
1991	80,000
1996	165,000
2000	>200,000

Source: London Docklands Development Corporation

5.61. It would be a great pity if the London Rail Studies did not prove to be a catalyst for real modernization of the London underground system and this must inevitably include new lines, particularly to cater for the poorly serviced areas in south-east and south-west London and also the Docklands area.

Buses

5.62. In spite of the problems associated with running buses through the increasingly congested streets of London, their use is now steadily rising. They could undoubtedly be developed to take a much more important role if reliability, average speed and passenger confidence could be improved. At present buses are generally perceived to be slow and unreliable. However if road pricing were introduced and balanced to the point where congestion were significantly reduced, the improvements to bus services could be sufficient to restore public confidence and improve demand and profitability. **The overriding advantage of bus services is that they can be routed almost anywhere and could quickly help to improve public transport in those areas of London which are at present poorly served.**

5.63. There are a number of options available to make bus travel more attractive and efficient. These include the installation of bus stops with arrival time indicators, electronic sensing to give buses priority at traffic lights; and the introduction of buses at the peak periods for season ticket holders only. The use of small buses and the introduction of collective taxis should also be considered.

5.64. The proposed deregulation of London buses must be considered with care. The experience in other UK cities is that deregulation causes a shift in the size of bus used from large double-deck units to midi and mini buses. Considerable disruption has been experienced in the short term with congestion being caused by a proliferation in the number of buses. In the longer term the situation tends to improve but some cities are still experiencing significant congestion. In general, the same number of passengers are being carried but in a larger number of smaller buses where practicable.

Roads in the conurbations

5.65. Road traffic congestion is endemic in most urban areas and with the forecast traffic increases, it will become worse unless very determined effects are made to deal with it. Congestion on the roads of our cities and towns has of course been with us for many years but the exercise of considerable ingenuity in traffic management together with various road improvements and bypasses, has prevented it from becoming intolerable and in some cases has actually improved matters. However the scope for further traffic management progress is becoming progressively less, especially in view of the tendency for discernible traffic flow improvement to attract additional cars on to the roads. **In many urban areas major new road building is no longer practicable except at unacceptable levels of financial and environmental cost.**

5.66. There are substantial effects on the transport systems from major land use changes and new development frequently places a strain on the local highway and public transport networks. These efforts have been exacerbated by the introduction of superstores and leisure parks on greenfield sites and within the urban framework through major downtown redevelopment. These sorts of development are most likely to take place where the regional economy is at its most buoyant and it is here that the road system is under the greatest pressure. **It follows that the full transport implications of major developments must be considered early in the planning stage and adequate contribution negotiated towards the cost of the necessary road improvements which may extend well beyond the immediate vicinity of the development.**

5.67. The goal of Government is to reduce casualties by one third by the year 2000. This has specific reference to congestion in urban areas where 70% of casualties occur and new initiatives will be needed if this target is to be reached. Area wide road safety schemes are being monitored by the Transport and Road Research Laboratory and first indications are that accidents in the areas treated are down by 10%. Traffic calming techniques are being widely used in Europe to reduce speeds and accidents on distributor and access roads.

Extent of the problem

5.68. Most of the larger conurbations in the country and many of the smaller towns are now experiencing some degree of congestion. Average city centre speeds during peak hours at places like Newcastle, Glasgow, Sheffield, Birmingham and Leeds are not much higher than the Central London peak hour speeds. Great ingenuity in traffic management has achieved genuine improvements in conditions. In Oxford, notable success in reducing congestion has been achieved through the use of a park-and-ride system. However there is wide variation between these larger conurbations with respect to their transportation problems and their options for dealing with congestion against changing patterns of economic performance, political aims, public preferences and land use.

5.69. In Manchester congestion problems identified in the 1960s led to large scale land use/transportation studies and thence to major

33

investment in highways. There is evidence that the benefits obtained from these improvements have been exhausted and congestion is once again returning. Similarly in Glasgow, an integrated transport plan was implemented in the 1960s but subsequently abandoned in the 1970s owing to a lack of financial support and complacency with the improvements in transportation resulting in an evaporation of public support for further road construction. Now at the end of the 1980s congestion has returned.

5.70. Land use changes are of great concern. An example in the Cardiff area is the scale of the Cardiff Bay Development Corporation's regeneration strategy. On full completion by 2003 as many as 250,000 additional person trips per day could be generated compared with the 1,000,000 person trips per day currently generated throughout the whole of South Glamorgan.

5.71. The population of many of the larger conurbations has been declining for several years as people move out of the centres to new developments on the periphery. These new housing locations rarely have worthwhile public transport services into the adjacent conurbations, so that journeys to work, shops, entertainment and so on must be undertaken by car thus adding to the radial flows. Lord Chilver, Chairman of Milton Keynes Development Corporation, suggested at a seminar at the ICE that the move away from centres of population is irreversible and should be recognized. Certainly it increases car travel into the conurbations and increases the problems of road congestion.

5.72. **In the smaller conurbations congestion is now becoming a problem as people move to the surrounding villages and travel to the local town for work, shopping and entertainment.** Typical are county towns such as Ipswich, Cambridge, Reading, Norwich and Exeter. Even in the small market towns problems are arising, although on a much smaller scale. Town centres designed for a totally different way of life and with narrow streets are becoming choked at busy times as people from the surrounding areas seek parking space near the centre. The problems are exacerbated by the increasing use of HGVs in rural areas as they are generally too large for the narrow roads and find it impossible to negotiate the small radius turnings without slowing down to walking pace and either blocking the whole road to negotiate the turn or running over the footpaths.

5.73. **Further problems arise from the recurring need to repair roads which were not built to take the traffic loading now being imposed upon them (particularly by HGVs), and the poor repair standards of the innumerable trenches which are opened up for the public service repairs and alterations which are an inevitable feature of new development.**

Options for action

5.74. **The best methods of dealing with congestion will vary from place to place, and must be the product of a careful study for each area. The options available are many, ranging from new road construction and improvements through traffic management to demand management in conjunction with public transport improvements.** As congestion varies in severity, so local perceptions of its penalties and the options for improvement also vary. For instance, one of the major tools available to reduce congestion in large conurbations is the use of parking restrictions and yet it is interesting to note that the survey report from the ICE local association in Yorkshire refers to the inter-city competition for prestigious town centre developments with a relaxation of parking restrictions being granted as an incentive. There is little doubt however that the trend is for road congestion to increase, and for the public pressure to deal with it to increase also.

5.75. In the larger conurbations, the options of new road building and improvements are limited and other solutions to the problems will be necessary. Traffic management systems of the type already mentioned undoubtedly **have an important part to play** and many traffic engineers are confident that congestion in their particular areas can be controlled by these means alone. **In the larger conurbations, some form of demand management in parallel with improved public transport facilities will prove to be necessary if really worthwhile improvements are to be achieved and, equally importantly, maintained.** Measures include the reduction of parking, particularly long stay parking and action to reduce illegal parking. Such measures must be planned in conjunction with demonstrable improvements in public transport.

5.76. In this latter connection **an increasing number of large conurbations are seriously studying the provision of light rail systems.** LRT has an attractive modern image which has been used successfully in urban regeneration. Car users are notably reluctant to transfer to other modes of transport, however LRT with its attractive modern image, high reliability and frequency of service has proved effective in attracting car drivers. In the UK the longest established LRT system is the Tyne and Wear Metro on which passenger journeys have increased from 14.1 million in 1981 to 44.9 million in 1987-88.

5.77. LRT systems have major cost advantages. Because of their ability to negotiate sharp curves and steep gradients they can be installed in existing urban environments with comparatively little disruption. The costs are small, an LRT station may cost 1/200 the cost of an underground station. The systems are flexible and can be run on existing or disused BR tracks or even along roads.

5.78. The use of light rail systems is increasing in large conurbations worldwide and there is a growing choice of systems. They offer a possible way of using private funding to improve congestion. Some planners have reservations about the value of LRT systems and Professor Hall has pointed out they cannot offer a general solution to the commuter journeys of an increasingly dispersed population. Nevertheless **LRT used as a park and ride facility offers a solution to the problems of congestion in central urban areas, and enabling pedestrianization schemes to go ahead.**

5.79. There is no disputing the success of the Docklands Light Railway system and in their December 1988 report on LRT systems, SERPLAN conclude that the Tyne and Wear Metro "has enhanced Newcastle city centre and some other centres. It has made travel easier and quicker and improved accessibility". Outside London, firm proposals have now been adopted for LRT systems to be installed in Bristol, Greater Manchester, Leeds, Sheffield and West Midlands

(Birmingham – Wolverhampton). Around 20 further conurbations outside London have such systems under consideration.

5.80. **For the smaller conurbations, dealing with road congestion is more amenable to solution by means of road improvements, bypasses and traffic management schemes with some occasional recourse to demand management.** In this latter connection **there is much value in the introduction of park-and-ride systems** operated in conjunction with traffic restraints such as parking restrictions.

Roads – inter-urban

5.81. The inter-urban road network is that which is also referred to as routes for longer distance traffic. These are the motorways and the green-backed sign primary routes. Of these only the motorways and trunk roads are a direct responsibility of the Government. The rest are local highway authority roads. Together they constitute the main arteries of movement for freight and people within the UK and to the ports, airports, and shortly the Channel Tunnel, giving access to European and worldwide markets.

5.82. The DTp, Scottish Development Department (SDD) and Welsh Office are together responsible for some 9500 miles of trunk roads and motorways. Although these roads represent only 4.3% of the total road network in Great Britain they carry over 33% of all traffic and nearly 60% of heavy goods traffic. The number of HGVs currently licensed reached a peak of 506,000 in 1979 and then fell steadily to a total 432,000 in 1985. Since then however the number has steadily increased. Traffic on motorways increased by 8% in 1988, which exceeds the DTp's high growth forecast, (although some of this increase may be attributable to the mild winter). Volume is growing at twice the rate of traffic on roads as a whole. From 1977 to 1987 motorway length increased by 33% and traffic on the motorways increased by 62%. (No separate figures for road length and traffic growth are available for those inter-urban, primary route roads which are the responsibility of local highway authorities.)

5.83. The DTp, the SDD and the Welsh Office together spend over £850 million a year on the construction of new motorways and trunk roads in Great Britain. It is relevant to note that an examination of capital expenditure on roads during the years 1978-79 to 1986-87 (based on the Public Expenditure Survey) shows that, in real terms, government expenditure on new construction and improvement has done little better than keep pace with inflation since 1981-82 and spending by local authorities has been of a similar order. The level of government spending has probably been influenced by the need to direct funds to structural renewal as a result of the deterioration of motorway pavements caused by the HGVs. Recently schemes worth over £6 billion were added to the existing roads programme, more than doubling its size.

Extent of the problem

5.84. **The inter-urban road network in the UK is becoming increasingly inadequate to satisfy the demands for freight and passenger movement which are so important to a modern, competitive economy on the threshold of the challenges of the integrated European market.** It is inadequate not only in extent but also in the capacity of increasing sectors. There are now more vehicles per kilometre of motorway in the UK than in any major country in Europe (at 50 km of motorway per million of population the UK compares with 115 km in France, 140 km in West Germany and 157 km in Belgium).

5.85. The growing congestion on motorways has been widely covered by the media. The overloading on the M25 has been well documented, as also have the problems on sections of the M1, M3, M4 and M5 and M6. On the M6 congestion of the corridor between Birmingham and Manchester/Liverpool has become widely criticized. The survey by our local associations has drawn attention to many lesser known problem areas throughout the inter-urban road network and it is apparent that such problem areas are increasing in number and severity. Even where measures are taken to relieve congestion they are not all as successful as the planners had hoped. An admittedly abnormal but nevertheless significant case in point is the Ilminster bypass on the A303 which was opened in July 1988 and is now the focus of greater traffic delays than those it was intended to cure.

Options for action

5.86. **One of the significant causes of congestion on the inter-urban road system are road accidents.** On motorways alone there were 5526 accidents in 1987 of which 1349 involved injuries which were fatal or serious. Where HGVs are involved the result is frequently prolonged delay and serious restriction to traffic flow. Quite apart from the congestion aspect, the toll of human life and injury on the entire road system represents a massive waste of resources to society. This is an area however where, given the political will, shorter term options are available to effect improvements. **Excessive speed and dangerous driving practices are major causes of accidents and much could be done to reduce these by the widespread introduction of surveillance cameras** and radar speed devices if they were accepted for use as legal evidence by the police and courts and if penalties were severe enough to deter. Goods vehicle tachometer records should be used as evidence to support charges for speeding and excessive driving hours. **There is also a strong case for reducing the speed limit for HGVs to its former level of 50 mph** in view of the excessive stopping distances when speeds exceed this level. Use of the tachometer records would overcome the problems which the police have in trying to enforce this limit. It is interesting to note that the police estimate that for an accident on a busy motorway occurring at a peak period the tailback grows at a rate of one mile every three minutes of blockage.

5.87. On hills, the slow speed of fully laden HGVs can obstruct the flow of traffic, causing major tailbacks. The provision of additional crawler lanes for HGVs should be considered. Where four lanes are provided, HGVs should be confined to the two near side lanes.

5.88. A further major cause of congestion is the incoming stream of traffic at interchanges and junctions and in many cases a shorter term option is available to improve this by ramp metering. The DTp tested **ramp metering** successfully at junction 10 on the M6 and **wider use should now be implemented as an urgent measure.** Junction closures are not recommended, however improvements in the provision of acceleration and deceleration lanes would reduce significantly the disruption to the flow of traffic.

5.89. **There are a number of other shorter term options which could** all contribute to the reduction of congestion in various situations such as: access control; better road marking, signing, and visual warnings of hazards; better management of lane closures and use of low traffic flow periods, particularly nighttime for repair work and maintenance; more rapid attention to vehicle breakdown and swift removal of carriageway debris on motorways. The West Midland police state that 15-16% of accidents on motorways in their area are attributable to debris. In order to reduce the impact of lane closures it is suggested that **hardshoulders should be strengthened to accept regular traffic flows.**

5.90. Although such shorter term measures have an important role they must necessarily be supported by long term initiatives. **There is a continuing need for public investment in targeted highway improvements and new routes.** The Highway Policy and Resources Division of the DTp carried out a review of the capacity of the motorway network commencing at the end of 1985. It was agreed that the concept of capacity of the network (which was thought to be difficult to determine because of the number of variables) should give way to one of stress on motorway links. The review concentrated on a speedy conclusion rather than great accuracy. DTp regional offices were involved and the aims of the survey were to identify those sections of motorway which would need relief over the next 10-15 years and to ensure that there was not a capacity crisis hanging over the network. Many of the results were incorporated in the Road Report *(National Roads England 1987)* when 12 motorway schemes were added to the programme

5.91. **The results of this survey should be monitored and a similar survey should be carried out for the whole primary route system** if necessary using outside resources to assist. In this connection the criteria for determining highway capacity adopted by the DTp are based on Annual Average Daily Flow (AADF) and design is based on the predicted flow 15 years after opening to traffic. When new roads take 15 years to come to fruition, it is tempting to assume that predictions must be taken 30 years ahead. However, this is unreasonable having regard to the technological changes in the last 30 years and future trends. AADF takes no account of peak hour or holiday flows, or the length of periods of congestion hold-up. Even on AADF the DTp acknowledged that nearly 20% of the motorway system was overloaded in 1986. Since then motorway traffic has increased by 14% in 1986-87 and by 13% in 1987-88. Bearing in mind the unreliability of 30 year forecasts, and the unpredictability of the economic and social changes that may occur in the period, it is preferable to plan against a shorter time scale, say a maximum of 15 years, providing sufficient flexibility to enable subsequent improvement to cater for the actual situation that develops. Criteria used by the Scottish Development Department appear to be in advance of those currently used by the DTp.

5.92. **The scope for private sector investment is restricted but should be encouraged wherever feasible. Every opportunity should be explored to encourage private sector or joint private/public expenditure where this would result in a net increase in actual expenditure on highways.** Given the high cost of constructing toll roads and the restricted opportunities, more consideration should be given to public refunding of private capital costs based on the actual traffic flows. In addition **greater benefits should be obtained from the increase in land values arising from or attributable to, public road construction. It is not suggested however that private investment will operate to provide new construction on a major scale.**

5.93. In reviewing the current approaches to road financing it is worth asking why an arbitrary division has been drawn between motorways/trunk roads and principal roads as they both carry large volumes of traffic on a small proportion of the network. Much of the principal road network running through urban areas is only to single carriageway standard, and there is evidence that these roads are suffering from a lack of investment in terms of new construction, reconstruction and maintenance (for example, the findings of the National Road Monitoring Condition Survey). It is not easy to see why trunk roads and motorways should be financed differently from principal roads, particulary as the latter are carrying such a substantial proportion of HGVs.

Railways – inter-urban

5.94. British Rail InterCity passenger volume has varied between quite narrow limits up until 1985. From a total of 11.7 billion passenger kilometres in 1977 it rose to 12.6 billion passengers kilometres in 1979 and then fell to 11.4 billion passenger kilometres in 1982. It rose again to 12.8 billion passenger kilometres in 1984 before dropping back to 12.5 billion passenger kilometres in 1985. Since that date however there has been a steady increase in passenger volume and the figure for the year 1987-88 was a total of 13.28 billion passenger kilometres. This latter figure represents a 5% increase over the previous year and is the highest recorded since InterCity services were introduced 22 years ago.

5.95. The increase in passenger volume can be attributed to a number of factors, the principal of which are the

(a) steady electrification of InterCity lines allowing greater speeds
(b) growth in long distance commuting
(c) introduction of more attractive off-peak fares, rail cards, and so on.

5.96. InterCity management is concentrating on improving standards of service, electrification of further routes and shortly the introduction of the new Class 90 and 91 high speed locomotives which will allow faster travel, so that it seems most probable that passengers volume will continue to increase.

5.97. As a result of the increases in passenger volume, **congestion in the form of overcrowding is occurring on the most heavily used parts of the network at times of maximum demand and in view of the pace of increase in passenger volume the situation seems likely to deteriorate in the immediate future unless more urgent action is taken to reduce overcrowding.**

5.98. In the provincial sector passenger traffic rose from 4.9 billion passenger kilometres in 1977 to 5.3 billion passenger kilometres in 1979, then fell to 4.6 billion passenger kilometres in 1982 and remained around this level until 1985 when a steady increase began and appears to be continuing. These increases have been achieved by

(a) the steady renewal of the Provincial sector fleet of trains
(b) increasing service frequency with the new trains: the Sprinter units also now operate over longer distances opening up new through journey opportunities
(c) the opening of additional stations: 70 stations have been opened or re-opened in the sector since it was created in 1982
(d) improved marketing.

5.99. Congestion is now occurring in various sectors of the provincial network and is likely to get worse if traffic continues to increase.

Extent of the problem

5.100. The Central Transport Consultative Committee, in its report of August 1988 said that **overcrowding on many lines in the InterCity and Provincial sectors has reached unacceptable levels.** In their Annual Report for 1987-88, British Rail refer only to the problem of overcrowding on some Cardiff Valley lines which has been relieved in part by providing extra coaches. It also refers briefly to the technical problems being experienced with the new two car Pacer diesel trains which have contributed to the problems in the Provincial sector.

5.101. In fact, **overcrowding has increased considerably on a growing number of lines or sections of lines,** such as Paddington – South Wales; the Midland Main Line; Liverpool – Hull; East Anglia – Lincoln; Ipswich – London; the North Wales routes; Kettering – St Pancras and the East Coast main line to name some of the bad examples. There are now quite severe cases on record, such as the Nottingham – Derby line where overcrowded trains have been unable to take all the passengers and some have been left behind on the platforms.

5.102. Various authorities have also expressed concern regarding the **safety problems which arise from overcrowded trains.** The National Union of Railwaymen has drawn attention to the safety of passengers on the new Sprinter diesel units when they are overcrowded and has commented upon various instances where severe overcrowding has endangered safety. There is little doubt that safety can be compromised by overcrowding and some of the King's Cross to Edinburgh trains provide good examples of this with corridors sometimes blocked by people and luggage.

Options for action

5.103. The major problem, as with all congestion, is that the supply of space is insufficient to meet the demand for it, but unlike the problems of congestion in other modes **the achievement of worthwhile improvement is relatively straightforward. The problem is essentially not one of limited track capacity but rather of insufficient rolling stock.** British Rail, in seeking to modernize its rolling stock has undertaken a building programme which is now providing new coaches on a regular programme basis. As these new coaches enter service, however, the old ones have been taken out of service. In the year 1987-88, over 10% of the old locomotive hauled carriages were taken out of service although many of them were less than 30 years old and were still serviceable.

5.104. While the need to modernize and dispose of old, shabby rolling stock as fast as possible is understandable, the action to do so has been rather too precipitate. If some of these old carriages had been retained for a further short period and others had been refurbished and retained as long as proved necessary they could have been used to help satisfy the burgeoning demand in the critical sectors of the networks. In this respect, while the introduction of the new Pacer and Sprinter units on Provincial sector has resulted in more frequent services, there is less provision of seats to each service so that little improvement has been achieved on the overloaded sections.

5.105. British Rail is now taking action to retain more old stock and InterCity has decided to refurbish some 150 old coaches, but this needs to be reinforced to achieve maximum benefit. It is possible that management budgetary rigidity has in the past been enforced at the expense of customer safety and comfort and without fully appreciating the entrepreneurial advantages of better provision. **Certainly the further retention of older rolling stock to help meet demand, and also where necessary the urgent extension of platforms to accommodate longer trains, would go a long way towards easing overcrowding.**

5.106. A further measure which may be worthwhile in the shorter term would be to adjust the fares system on the overloaded routes to minimize overcrowding.

Channel Tunnel

5.107. The opening of the Channel Tunnel in 1993, providing direct access to the massive European Community market, could prove to be of inestimable value to the UK and have particular relevance to the economic regeneration of areas of urban and inner city decay. Its full potential, however, can only be exploited if its development is handled with vision and entrepreneurial skill, backed by adequate resources. In Europe its potential appears to have been recognized fully. Huge financial resources are being allocated to the planning and construction of a TGV Network which will link Brussels, Paris, Amsterdam and Cologne to the Tunnel with trains running at 300 km/hour in the 1990s. More inter-city railway was built or approved in Europe in 1988 than at any time since the start of the age of the airliner, according to Jane's Annual Survey.

5.108. BR carried out a study of long term route and terminal capacity and published a report in July 1988. It concluded that, after allowing for the existing proposals to extend station platforms and train formations and to replace existing domestic rolling stock with high capacity units, the effect of capacity limitations on the existing Southern Region routes, arising from the addition of trains to the Tunnel will start to be felt within ten years of the Tunnel opening to traffic. If actual traffic corresponds to the forecasts prepared for BR by MVA Consultancy in 1987, BR state that there will be no financial justification for providing extra route and terminal capacity until well into the next century. If actual traffic corresponds to the forecasts prepared by SETEC for Eurotunnel in 1986, financial justification for providing extra route and terminal capacity is brought forward to around the turn of the century. BR have endeavoured to determine the best acceptable route for a high speed passenger line from the Tunnel to London against determined opposition from Kent residents. A further study has selected the King's Cross low level option as the best choice for a second London terminal.

5.109. **The additional road traffic which will be generated by the opening of the Tunnel and the operation of the Eurotunnel shuttle will cause further pressures on already congested roads.** The DTp plans to construct or improve much of the motorway infrastructure serving the Tunnel, including widening the M25 and the motorways leading away from London to the regions. Work has already begun on the construction of the missing section of the M20 between Ashford and Maidstone, and the two lane Maidstone bypass section is to be widened.

5.110. The regions north of London have expressed considerable concern regarding the limited perceived benefits which will accrue to their industry and people. For passenger and freight traffic from the North to the Tunnel, London is a blockage to the direct route which they need for fast transit direct to the Continent and they fear that most of the benefits of the Tunnel will fall to the South East with only limited benefits for the regions north of London.

Extent of the problem

5.111. The existing domestic rail services through Kent to London have seen significant growth in passenger traffic over the past few years and they are now amongst the most heavily overcrowded lines in the country during peak periods. The BR forecasts, both of future domestic traffic and of the passenger traffic demand for international services, are conservative. In this latter category, BR has adopted a forecast of passenger traffic through the Tunnel totalling 13.3 million per annum by 1995 which is below all the forecasts by MVA, SETEC or Eurotunnel.

5.112. **The existing Southern Region Network will be inadequate to accommodate the Channel Tunnel traffic from an earlier date than is anticipated in BR plans. As a result congestion on these lines will increase significantly before a new line can be brought into service, unless the programme is brought forward.**

5.113. In the freight market BR aims to attract a 20% share of the unitized traffic between Britain and the Continental Zone of influence of the Tunnel (that is, south of a line extending along the northern border of Belgium and thence across mid Germany). 75% of this freight is expected to originate from outside London and the South East, the bulk of it from manufacturing industry in the Midlands and the North. However BR is not proposing a fast through freight line to the North. Freight trains will run over the existing lines and when a high speed passenger line is constructed, BR consider that sufficient capacity will be available on the domestic lines to accommodate all the planned freight train movements.

5.114. The conservative forecasts of future freight traffic hardly reflect the entrepreneurial drive for business which should be launched by BR. Should domestic passenger and freight traffic exceed the BR forecasts, increased congestion on the domestic lines will no doubt arise even after the new high speed line (reserved for passenger trains only) is in operation.

5.115. The opening of the Tunnel will result in considerable increases in both car and road freight traffic. The extent of this traffic increase will depend upon the success or failure of BR to attract business and the relevant traffic shares secured by the ferries and the Eurotunnel shuttles. Conservative forecasts predict an average flow of 20,000 - 24,000 vehicles per day using the Tunnel in 2008 while ferries would continue to attract some 10,000 vehicles per day through Kent. An ever increasing volume of HGVs is forecast with or without the Channel Tunnel. While the DTp plans to improve the road links from London to the Tunnel, the major problem will be increasing congestion on the M25. This blockage and that represented by the morass of the Greater London area causes justifiable concern in the industrial Midlands and the North.

Options for action

5.116. **The construction of the high speed passenger line should proceed with all possible speed.** The understandable concern of local protesters should be met by route adjustments and environmental protection measures which should attract a measure of government funding support, even at the expense of an amendment to Section 42 of the Channel Tunnel Act. Accelerated construction techniques should be adopted to achieve the earliest possible completion date for this line and the construction of a second London terminal at King's Cross as proposed by BR. This terminal would provide the opportunity for through routing which could satisfy the aspirations of the Midlands and the North.

5.117. **The problems of freight traffic loom large.** The interests of a dynamic modern commercial sector demand the provision of reliable high speed freight services. If these could be provided via the Tunnel and across the Continental network with easy and convenient terminal accesses and fast connecting routes to all regions of the UK, the opportunities to benefit the national economy and the BR business and to reduce road freight could be very attractive. To this end necessary initiatives by BR would be

(a)   **the development of a fast freight route to the North,** bypassing the constraints of London
(b)   a study of the actual costs of clearing such a route
(c)   **the rapid development of the use of intermodal systems** such as swap bodies (offering complete interchangeability of payload without lift-on, lift-off cranage); piggyback (carrying complete road trailers on rail wagon flats) and trailer trains (trailers with both road and rail bogeys). With these systems transfer between road and rail can take place literally on a strip of concrete beside a railway siding
(d)   **the development of high speed, small wheel bogies** to enable larger payloads to be carried within the existing loading gauge
(e)   the construction, where the opportunities for traffic enhancement occur, of **additional Freightliner depots for container services.**

5.118. To achieve maximum benefit from the Tunnel and 1992, and to avoid even worse road congestion on the M25, provision should be made in the long term road programme for feasibility studies of schemes which have been mooted recently. These schemes include

(a)   the **East Coast Motorway** (serving as a national distributor and linking with the East Coast ports)
(b)   a **second orbital motorway outside the M25** (or perhaps a triangular motorway with a southern base)
(c)   a motorway parallel to M6 between Birmingham and Preston.

ANNEX

Annex A. Technical aspects
A1. Thresholds of unacceptability

Definition of unacceptable congestion

1. What may be unacceptable congestion has no universal definition. It varies according to whether it is perceived by road users, bus passengers, passengers on British Railways, London Underground, a metro system, or by non-users faced with its side effects. It also varies with whether travel is

(a) inter-urban or inter-city
(b) rural, in and between smaller towns and villages
(c) within conurbations, cities and larger towns
(d) within London.

2. The inter-urban road network is that which is also referred to as routes for longer distance traffic. These are the motorways and green-back signed primary routes. Of these, only the motorways and trunk roads are a direct responsibility of the Government. The rest are local highway authority roads. Together they constitute the main arteries of movement for freight and people within UK and to the ports and airports giving access to Europe and world-wide markets. Congestion on the inter-urban network is perceived when delays add to the journey times which are normally achievable in uncongested conditions on the better motorways and all-purpose roads respectively, thereby upsetting the certainty of being able to complete journeys at high average speeds. The criterion, therefore, is overall speed of travel, converted into total time for a journey.

3. Rural roads comprise that extensive network of all classes of road which serve towns, villages and the rural community. Some of these roads are busy cross-country routes, which may seem to be of little less importance than the primary routes in the vicinity. The inter-urban network as defined above is of substantially higher status, being of national importance. It follows that the rural network requires less rigorous standards by which congestion should be judged. Overall speed of travel does not appear to be the appropriate criterion. Congestion is perceived as unacceptable delay through points on the network (mainly junctions) compared with uncongested conditions. Therefore, the criterion is time lost at individual points, qualified by the volume of traffic affected.

4. The two urban area descriptions distinguish London from cities with substantial populations and national economic significance, where there is potential for or there are existing urban mass transit systems. On the whole, congestion is not the problem in conurbations and major cities that it is in London. Therefore, the former would be expected to set lower thresholds for unacceptable congestion than would London. Nor is it likely that any criterion expressed in absolute terms would fit the needs or experience of every city.

5. There is a transition from inter-urban to urban as roads enter cities. Those cities which are least affected by congestion would be perceived as those into which main access routes went closest to the city centre while still meeting the inter-urban criterion. Other access

routes and distributor roads within urban cores can also only be judged by travel speed criteria, although they would be set at substantially lower levels than would be appropriate for the inter-urban road network. It would be appropriate that the criteria should correlate with what travel speeds can be secured by the use of existing or potential rapid transit systems.

6.   Road congestion adversely affects bus operations, so that timetables are either not adhered to or are adjusted to undesirably slow timings. The criteria for buses should be, at worst, the same as those set for road traffic in general, except that there is a general presumption in favour of higher criteria that buses should be given preferential treatment.

7.   Buses also share some of the more notable forms of congestion which afflict London Underground, commuter rail and some other parts of urban rail systems. These include overcrowding and discomfort in vehicles, stations, interchange subways, ticket areas and related public facilities, coupled with delays to and loss of frequency of the services themselves. Definition of unacceptable congestion on these systems is clouded by long run acceptance in inner city areas of levels of crowding and discomfort which would be considered intolerable for inter-city and commuter rail travel.

8.   Therefore, realistic definitions of the criteria of unacceptable congestion of urban public transport must be partly subjective. Nevertheless, criteria could relate to availability of seats for journeys of specified length, space per standing passenger, scaled to length of time, proximity to the densest part of the system and time of day, space per person waiting and moving on platforms, in subways and other circulation areas, queuing times for tickets, and waiting times and frequency of services.

9.   Suburban rail may provide services very similar, indeed indistinguishable from, the urban public transport systems discussed above or be principally the provider of commuter services from the outer urban area and beyond. Whatever may have come to be users expectations of services of this kind, there is a good case for their being judged by criteria set substantially higher than for underground services. Nevertheless, the criteria would be expressed in similar terms.

10.   The criteria for InterCity rail and other longer distance BR services should be set higher still. Standing at any time should be unacceptable.

11.   The report to which this annex attaches is not addressing congestion within ports and airports or of the airways. Ports and airports, however, are key focal points of transport infrastructure and access to them is of great national significance. Access routes to ports and airports by road or rail should normally be of inter-urban standards and be judged accordingly against the criteria discussed in paragraph 2.

A2. Road pricing

Introduction

1. Congestion arises from an imbalance between the supply and demand for road space. The effective price to each additional user at congested periods is zero – the only force acting to bring demand in line with supply is the personal inconvenience and time wasted by each individual user. Road users presently pay taxes in the form of petrol tax and road fund licence, there is no direct pricing of road use. In congested conditions each additional user places costs on other users of the system which far outweigh his own costs. The result is that road space is allocated by queuing and without any constraint on demand the inevitable result is frequent traffic jams. Queuing is an exceedingly inefficient method of operating and managing the road network.

2. The price mechanism has been put forward as a means of regulating the demand for road space to the available supply. It has attracted much controversy. Some say that to abandon the free access of roads in favour of access by ability to afford does not allocate according to need; that it penalizes the poor and that the traffic it is intended to control – principally single occupancy car commuters – will merely transfer the increased cost on to their companies. Others say that the price mechanism does allocate according to need, that while the less well off may not be able to afford to travel to work by car, travel by bus – which tends to be used by the lower income groups of society – will become far more efficient as the roads clear and traffic speeds increase.

Systems available
Toll booths

3. Though a tried and tested technique, operating in many of the UK's esturial crossings such as the Dartford Tunnel or the Humber Bridge, toll booths have high operating costs, a large land take, and cause significant disruption to traffic. It is therefore unlikely that a comprehensive system of road pricing could be based on a network of toll booths.

Daily tickets

4. A system of stickers to be displayed by cars wishing to use certain roads at peak hours is operated in Singapore. The effect of introduction of the scheme was dramatic with the number of cars entering the city core being cut by 44% overall and at peak times by 65%. Stickers are a simple and low cost system – enforcement costs are said to amount to 5% of revenue. The drawbacks are the cost of administration, monitoring and the lack of flexibility.

Automatic vehicle identification

5. Automatic vehicle identification systems (AVI) are based on a centralized computer which monitors the passage of cars past specific points on the road network. Each car is equipped with an electronic number plate which allows the car to be identified by the central computer as it passes the toll point. Drivers are invoiced on a periodic basis, motorists receiving bills itemized for each occasion they passed a specific toll point; a charge which could be varied according to the time of day, the direction of travel, or the prevailing congestion. Perhaps the best analogy is with a telephone bill.

6.   The problems with the system are as follows.

(a)   Capital cost – each vehicle must be equipped with an electronic number plate. A problem arises with vehicles not equipped with number plates such as those from overseas. A system of plate rental could be implemented.

(b)   Privacy – because the system operates on the basis of identifying the whereabouts of a specific vehicle at a specific time, concern has been expressed as to a central authority being able to keep tabs on the whereabouts of its citizens.

On-vehicle meters

7.   The second alternative method of road pricing is to use a meter installed in each car. The system of charging would be based around the meter being read at periodic intervals as in the case of an electricity or gas meter or alternatively meters could be operated by a card similar to the GPO Phone Card system, or by the new smart card technology currently being developed by banks.

8.   The meters would be activated by road side devices or alternatively by using area based radio frequency transmissions such as the cellular car phone network. The charge rate could be varied according to location and time with the cost indicated on a display in the driver's dashboard.

9.   The principal advantage over the AVI technology is the avoidance of the civil liberty issue. The disadvantages are the same – that is the capital cost and the problem of cars not equipped with a pricing device.

Cellular phone network

10.   Arguments that road pricing infringes civil liberties have been raised but they apply equally to car phones. The car phone network is based on a system of local cells each with its own transmitter and receiver. To make a phone call to a car phone requires the phone network to have knowledge of the whereabouts of the car in relation to the cell network. This is achieved by the car phone automatically advising a central switching centre whenever it moves from one cell to another. The size of a cell varies from tens of kilometres in the countryside to fractions of kilometres within cities. There exists already a system in the UK which enables the monitoring of the whereabouts of individual cars – provided they have the necessary equipment.

Application

11.   Road pricing can be applied by establishing a cordon around central city areas. Passing through the cordon activates the pricing mechanism. While simple to operate this method of application has the disadvantage that it creates edge effects including the parking of cars in large numbers possibly in residential ares and people living around the boundary would have a case to argue as to the fairness of charges. Furthermore much traffic is generated internally and unless passing through the cordon would be able to travel without charge. In major conurbations the problem lies in the fact that there are many centres and the establishment of a large number of cordons around each centre would be required. The technology of electronic road pricing enables the problems of edge effects to be overcome by allowing the pricing level to be adjusted continuously according to location and the prevailing level of congestion. Against this is the loss of certainty, that a driver will not know the exact cost of making a given journey.

Road pricing in practice

12.   Road pricing schemes are known to have been implemented or are under consideration in the following countries

Country	System	Comments
Singapore	Stickers	System in operation and working
California	AVI	System under consideration
Hong Kong	AVI	System delayed for civil rights reasons
Holland	On-vehicle metering	Under consideration

Annex B. Administrative aspects
B1. Land use planning and development control

1. During the late 1960s, following American practice, it became fashionable to undertake transportation studies, using complex mathematical models to synthesize traffic flows and forecast growth. The outputs from these studies were plans for the future of transport in the areas studied. They became basic input to structure plans and local plans.

2. Intrinsic to these studies was the evaluation of existing land uses and of various alternative land use scenarios for the future. The models could not work without input on land use and related parameters, such as population structure, jobs, car ownership, trip making habits and public transport provision. Many of these studies were named land use transportation studies.

3. Land use is a fundamental determinant of the quantity of movement for which the transport system should provide. This leads to a presumption that control of land use can have a bearing on the provision of transport.

4. Viewed from a strategic level, that is nationally, regionally and area-wide (if this is taken to mean a coherent sub-region, equivalent to a conurbation or part of a county), it is clear that major new developments do have a significant bearing on the provision of transport. A third London airport, substantial development of new housing in expanded villages and towns, a new industrial or commercial complex each has a potential to generate trips for which there may or may not be space in the pre-existing transport system.

5. At issue, however, is whether the control mechanisms available to transportation authorities make a balancing of new developments with transport provision possible and whether there are not other and more potent influences which are the actual determinants of demand on the transport system.

6. There can be no doubt that socio-economic changes have been the principal driving force behind the ever increasing demand for transport and consequential congestion of the transport system. Land use changes have followed so that now much development control activity is devoted to resisting proposals which seek to disrupt the frameworks set by planning authorities.

7. This is not true of the whole of the UK, of course, because there are many areas outside London and the South-East where planning authorities are actively promoting development and using all available techniques to attract developers and create jobs. Nevertheless, it evident that it is where congestion of the transport system is at its worst that planning authorities on the whole are most engaged in rearguard actions against further development.

8. The question which arises is whether development control can be used to curtail the growth in congestion or even reverse the trend.

9. Where it is clear that an additional development will result in the overloading or breakdown of the transportation system it is possible successfully to refuse planning permission or secure sufficient investment in the transport system from the developer to avert the breakdown. Under these circumstances a balance between transport and development can be maintained.

10. In the situation where the individual proposal is one of many similar proposals but in itself does not have the last straw characteristic or where the developer will not agree to provide sufficient investment in the transport system, the situation is more difficult to resolve.

11. It has long been assumed that, transport on the whole being a publicly funded service, transport authorities would pick up and deal with growth in demand. Developers have tended to argue, with some justification, that they pay their rates and taxes and that they should not be charged again for the added costs they impose on the transport authorities.

12. The pressures for more movement have further blurred the boundary between the natural growth for which provision must be made out of rates and taxes and the extraordinary growth which might be properly laid at the door of developers. Planning authorities are very well aware of this dilemma and must argue it through each time a developer makes his application for planning approval.

13. It is quite clear that the tide of new development is running so strongly in London and the South-East and in some other parts of the country that an increase in congestion is inevitable. At local planning authority level, the best they can do, working closely with the highway and other transport authorities is to maximize the planning gain contributions from the developers to improvements in transport. They work within existing planning frameworks and there is no certainty that these will not be breached on appeal.

14. The question, therefore, is whether these planning frameworks are up to the task of holding development at levels within the capability of the transport system. For the reasons discussed, it is clear that they cannot and will not as presently constituted. There are no regional or sub-regional strategies with teeth and in any case planning controls are not intended or devised as shorter term instruments of socio-economic engineering.

15. Planning and development control, therefore, can only have a strategic effect in the short term if new developments can be made to pay to avoid any direct consequences for congestion and, better, provide a net improvement.

16. For the foreseeable future, development control will continue to be a mechanism for minimizing damage and maximizing planning gain, within the framework of properly evaluated and expressed regional, sub-regional and local strategies. Transport systems, their competence and adequacy, the extent of existing and prospective congestion must all feature in these strategies, because, if they do not, the impact of development proposals cannot be judged.

17.   If transport strategies are to be in place, each transport authority, working in collaboration with others, must understand the way the available systems are working, what are the actual and potential crisis points and what may be appropriate action to meet future demand. This suggests that the land use transportation studies are an essential element in development of planning.

B2. Long preparation times for road infrastructure

1.   The five stages in the implementation of transport proposals are

(a)   identification of the actual or potential problem or indication of a general intention to provide
(b)   exploration of alternatives and selection of preferred solution
(c)   order procedures, planning permission and public inquiry
(d)   detailed design, preparation of contract documents and tender period
(e)   construction.

2.   It is widely asserted that these stages can consume 15 years or more. This is borne out in the following analysis, but Stage (a) is shown to be the most unpredictable.

3.   Stage (b) can become lengthy, because it involves public consultations on alternatives, sometimes with intensive activity directed towards frustration of a decision on a preferred solution. Good marketing of the alternatives, on the other hand, can minimize controversy. This stage normally consumes between 18 months and three years, although in very controversial cases it can be much longer. Only where there is widespread public support for the only available solution can this stage be minimized.

4.   Stages (c) and (d) can overlap to some extent, if no serious upset is expected in Stage (c). Where Stage (b) has been very controversial, however, a hard fought and long-running public inquiry is almost inevitable and no assumptions can be made about the likely outcome. An adverse inspector's report can put a scheme back into Stage (b). Without the need for a public inquiry, it is possible to get through Stages (c) and (d) in two years, but an inquiry followed by lengthy consideration of the inspector's report can extend this period up to five years.

5.   Stage (e) is very dependent on the size and complexity of the works and the time of year at which it is possible to start. Typically contracts last two years, but the range spreads from 18 months to three years.

6.   The timespan from the start of the serious study of alternative solutions to completion of construction, (Stages (b)-(e) inclusive) ranges from five years for a simple and uncontroversial scheme to at least eleven years for large, complex and probably controversial projects. Eleven years could easily grow to 14 or 15 if the Secretaries of State agree with an inspector's rejection of a first set of orders and start the consultation process again with revised alternatives.

7.   However, Stage (b) is very rarely the genesis of the scheme. Identification of the need for action of some kind may arise in many different ways and at any time in relation to widespread recognition that there is a problem looking for a solution. There may never be widespread accord that there is a problem or that the type of solution

suggested is appropriate. Transportation authorities, therefore, operate ranking systems which list proposals in orders of priority. The list grows as new problems are identified, some displacing long standing candidates for attention. The list shrinks proportionally to the rate at which finance is thought likely to be available for implementation and by removing proposals which are judged to be too controversial.

8. In recent times, when public sector capital expenditure programmes have been under heavy constraint, some local highway authorities have eliminated all priorities from their lists of schemes, alleging that there was too much uncertainty and too little cash. It follows that although a problem is recognized and there are some ideas about how it might be solved, many years may pass before it emerges from the list into Stage (b). This is sometimes referred to as firm programming. It is a decision to commence serious preparation and to make the finance available in due course for actual construction.

9. It is evident that Stage (a) can be of almost any duration. This is true equally of DTp schemes and those of local transportation authorities. It is very unlikely that less than three years would elapse from recognition of the problem to a firm commitment to seek a solution. It is easy to understand how a rural bypass, primarily for environmental reasons, might make no progress for 10, 15 or even 20 years, when in competition with expensive and complex schemes to relieve congestion on primary routes or in urban areas.

10. Assuming a quick start, total time could range from 8-14 years, but for all the reasons discussed Stages (a)-(e) together very often take much longer.

11. As has been suggested, the scope for dramatic time savings in Stages (b)-(e) is limited by the procedures that are thought to be necessary and the determination of objectors to make maximum use of them. Where there is widespread public support for a proposal, time can be saved, suggesting that good promotion of both the need to find a solution and of the most appropriate solution could be helpful in speeding up implementation.

12. The adoption of procedures closer to those applied to hybrid bills in Parliament might offer useful time savings. However, the key element is the lead time, that is Stage (a). An acceleration of the rate at which schemes passed out of Stage (a) into Stage (b) would call for an immediate increase in the availability of professional resources and a commitment to an equivalent increase in contract expenditure in 1-5 years time. It is that longer term commitment which Governments and local authorities are very reluctant to make. Until they do, preparation times will remain inordinately long.

13. The major obstacle to the early resolution of objections to schemes is the level of compensation. Given the expense of public enquiries there is a good deal to be said for increasing compensation level to the point where objections diminish. This is hard to define but it should be approachable on a basis in which negotiations should not be restricted unilaterally before commencement by unrealistic limits on what can be offered. Delay can of itself be very costly.

B3. Organization and funding of transport infrastructure: an international perspective

Extracts from OECD paper: Managing and financing urban infrastructure 6 April 1988

Organization

1. In the USA, the granting of federal aid is dependent on the establishment within each conurbation of a body responsible for consultation and five year indicative planning – a metropolitan planning organization, in which the organizing authorities (local authorities) can be represented.

2. In Germany, a large number of co-operation arrangements enable public authorities to co-ordinate programming and the carrying through of investments on a city-wide scale. The most complete form of integration involves the establishment of private companies in which the local authorities have a majority shareholding: authorities participate with these companies in discussions at a community level.

3. It is often left to central government to create authorities to organize infrastructures for whole urban areas, this is so for example in France, the UK, the USA, Spain, Italy, Portugal, Netherlands, Belgium. In Germany, Austria, Sweden, Switzerland integration is a achieved on the basis of voluntary agreements at local level.

4. In nearly all countries enterprises are controlled by the public or semi-public sectors. France and Japan are exceptions but, in all the developed world's large cities, investment decisions are no longer left to the private businessman who has also often lost responsibility for operating risks. Public authorities are becoming therefore increasingly involved and while making good the operating deficits of enterprises, participate in the funding of network extension and modernization. The forms taken by such contribution to funding vary widely depending on the country involved, and in all cases the state participates in the financing of major network investment, (railway lines, dedicated roads) together with the local organizing authority.

Funding

5. In the USA, federal aid represented 67% of investment expenditure in 1982. The remaining one third of investment expenditure is provided by state and local authorities.

6. The Germany, federal and *Länder* (*Länder* – regional government) subsidies for urban railway construction or extension are up to 100% of the cost of such projects, 70% from the federal government, 30% from the *Länder*.

7. It is rare in OECD countries for the operating expenditure of transport services to be covered by user charges since prices within this sector are set with reference to non-financial objectives such as encouraging the use of mass transport. It would therefore seem unrealistic to count on prices to finance investment in this sector. The price elasticity of transport demand is however very much lower than one in absolute terms which would justify an increase in prices, a trend moreover which can already be seen or is being encouraged in a

growing number of countries including the Netherlands, the UK, and New Zealand.

Cross financing

8.   The deficit recorded by local community transport companies in Germany is made good by the profits from other municipal services.

Special infrastructure taxes

9.   The USA employs a more flexible form of the local infrastructure taxes found in Europe. They have a precise target which puts them somewhere between taxes and user charges. They make it possible to apply local taxation in a much more tightly defined manner and in time (the tax is abolished when the loan granted finance construction has been repaid).

In kind or cash exactions

10.   This method of infrastructure financing is also very similar to local infrastructure taxes, for example an offer by a property developer to obtain or expedite the approval of local authorities for a given project or an entry charge levied on all applicants for building permits.

11.   Exactions take different forms: land, rights-of-way, construction of intersections and roads adjacent to the development, a proportion of dwellings included in commercial complexes, or low rent housing in residential developments.

12.   The land readjustment policy commonly used in Japan is a method of substantially reducing the land costs of infrastructure development. Once the space required for the infrastructure has been reserved, land situated within a readjustment area is reapportioned between property owners. Part of the area is retained by the authorities and resold to help pay the cost of implementing the programme. The size of original property holdings thus decreases but the increase in value resulting from the readjustment (new public infrastructures, roads and access to public transport) compensates for this.

General Infrastructure taxation

13.   In most countries taxes and charges on vehicles or motor fuels serve to finance infrastructure investment.

14.   Since 1982, in France the revenue from a surtax on fuel has been paid into a special fund for major projects relating to road and mass transport infrastructures. The civil engineering work for metro lines is subsidized to the tune of 40%, and a 50% subsidy is given for networks reserved for mass transport.

15.   In Germany federal subsidies to develop the road network and mass transport are also taken from the revenue from a surtax on fuel and oil, the revenues being divided equally between the road network and public transport. In addition the *Länder* obtain resources from an annual tax on vehicles.

Financing by indirect beneficiaries

16.   Several countries have introduced taxes on beneficiaries other than users. These other beneficiaries include employers, tradesmen, promoters, property owners and car drivers. In France, firms with more than nine employees contribute by means of the transport levy to mass transport expenditure, either by covering the fare reductions from which employees benefit or by contributing to operating and investment costs. This specific tax, first introduced in the Paris region

has gradually been extended to all towns of more than 30,000 inhabitants. In 1982, employers paid for approximately one quarter of operating expenses in the Paris region and for 30% of the operating expenses and 40% of investment expenditure in the provinces. In the USA, the local authorities control, manage, or tax the land adjacent to new railway lines and the revenue arising therefrom is used to finance new infrastructures.

Annex C. Economic aspects

C1. A market approach to road use

1.   Recently there has been considerable interest in the proposition that transport should be subject to market forces wherever possible. If the discipline of the market were to complement and eventually supersede the regulatory apparatus of the state, a more efficient outcome would result for the road user (the consumer). In practice, the market for transportation, where it can be said to exist at all, is inefficient and distorted.

2.   Economic theory dictates that all modes of transport, especially road and rail, should operate in the framework of a unified market to maximize opportunities for competition. If the market is efficient it will enable resources to be distributed in accordance with the wishes and needs of the community. An optimal pattern of resource allocation will then result making it impossible to make someone better off without making someone else worse off. A perfectly efficient pattern of resource allocation is inherently implausible, but it may be possible to improve significantly on the present pattern.

3.   One of the key conditions for an efficient market is that prices should be as near as possible to costs, especially marginal costs. This is the same as saying that the value the community places on something, which is reflected in the price it is prepared to pay for it, should equal the cost of the resources used to produce it. These must include all the resources used – not just obvious things like labour or capital, but external effects (externalities, in economic jargon) like noise or pollution. When this does not happen there is said to be market failure.

4.   Market failure is the rule rather than the exception in much of the economy, and road transportation is no different. The key factors obstructing the functioning of the market are

(a)   the absence of a price mechanism to allocate road space between road users

(b)   the absence of a system of road charging based on marginal costs

(c)   the problem of externality-type costs.

5.   A market-led solution to congestion would have to tackle all three of these.

Road pricing

6.   The biggest change a move like this would entail would be on the use of pricing policies to allocate road space. These would have to be on a pay-as-you-go basis. At present, too much road space is demanded by private motorists because part of the price of access to roads constitutes a lump-sum tax (Vehicle Excise Duty), by definition invariant to vehicle use.

7.   It would be necessary to shift the burden of motorcar taxation towards taxes imposed on the actual use of vehicles (for example VAT

on petrol and Petrol Duty). In parallel with this, serious consideration should be given to the introduction of road pricing.

Externalities

8.   Road vehicles impose substantial costs on the community. These range from the pervasive and intrusive effects of noise, pollution, dirt and vibration, to the costs of injuries and fatalities which occur as a result of accidents. There would be major disagreements on the valuation of these externalities; it would be difficult to reach an agreed position of consensus.

9.   It might be the case, providing these externalities can be valued correctly, that total road taxation would have to increase. It would be important to vary taxation by class of road user in proportion to the costs imposed on society. This might mean

(a)   large increases in taxation for HGVs
(b)   increases in road transport costs
(c)   abolition of company car tax allowances
(d)   higher motor vehicle taxation or road pricing in built-up areas or remote sparsely populated areas
(e)   significant changes in industrial and residential patterns in view of the size of transport spending in consumer expenditure.

10.   Road pricing would be the best way to impose these new pay-as-you-go type taxes (there is no point in specifying a market solution to transportation if it is not accompanied by road pricing – markets cannot function properly without a price mechanism). The use of the price mechanism to regulate demand would also affect income distribution and the access of different income groups to transport. Compensation (through improving public transport systems) might be desirable in certain circumstances.

C2. Costs of congestion

Introduction

1.   Given the importance of road and rail, congestion, which can be characterized as the systematic disruption of transportation networks by overload, is capable of generating substantial wastage when it leads to excess consumption of resources (for example through prolongation of journey times). Before explaining and accounting for these costs it is necessary to define what is understood by a congestion cost. This immediately raises the problem of seeking a satisfactory definition of congestion. The discussion which follows relates to road transport only (congestion costs on rail would be even more difficult to evaluate).

2.   There is no satisfactory objective and absolute definition of road transport congestion which can be used as a basis for calculating congestion costs. Congestion is a relative concept because it is mostly measured and assessed by comparing the progress of a traffic flow in congested conditions with some notion of how the same traffic flow would progress in uncongested free-flow conditions. Congestion costs should rise as road networks (and hence optimal free-flow traffic conditions) improve even if there is no change in actual traffic conditions.

3.   A related problem with many estimates of congestion costs is that they are calculated using a very small sample size. This is perhaps inevitable given the scale of road traffic (an acceptable sample size for statistical inference would have to include thousands of motor vehicles).

4.   To the extent that some of the monetary estimates of the cost of congestion are calculated on this basis it is necessary to regard them as being no more than very approximate estimates of the size of the costs generated by congestion. How large are they likely to be and where are they liable to fall?

Measurement of costs

5.   The main potential costs to road users arising from congestion are

(a)   lost output, lost deliveries and lost appointments
(b)   increase in holdings of inventories
(c)   increase in other costs of running businesses (because of uncertainty)
(d)   increase in vehicle operating costs
(e)   lower productivity of road vehicles
(f)   waste of paid working time lower productivity of road drivers
(g)   waste of non-working time
(h)   environmental costs such as fumes and noise
(i)   increased costs to pedestrians and cyclists
(j)   increased driver stress
(k)   increased accidents
(l)   lower levels of amenity in journeys
(m)   restriction of development and redevelopment.

6.   Congestion will encourage businesses (mostly retail outlets) to hold a higher level of inventories as a safeguard against supply

disruption induced by congestion. Little is known about the size of this effect in practice, but with retail turnover approaching £110 billion per year, the cost to the retail sector of interest charges needed to finance an inventory equivalent to turnover for a week would be about £200 million.

7.   Reducing congestion would eventually reduce the operating costs of road freight hauliers and this would be one of the principal economic benefits from tackling congestion. With road freight about 6% of GDP, a 10% fall in transport costs would boost GDP by about £3000 million. In some areas of the country the GDP effect might be even larger – a CBI survey suggests that additional costs arising from delivery, service and sales are on average 20% higher in London and the South East than anywhere else in the UK, largely because of congestion. Further evidence that road freight congestion in the South East is a particularly costly problem comes from the Freight Transport Association which recently published a survey estimating the cost per year in congestion per lorry using the M25 as approximately £1000. (Congestion on other types of roads and other motorways outside the congested South East is not as serious as on M25, but with an HGV population of over 400,000 it is clear that if the average congestion cost per lorry is only one tenth that on the M25, the cost to the nation's economy runs into many millions of pounds.)

8.   Congestion increases the frequency of traffic accidents although it reduces their severity. The total cost of vehicle accidents to business exceeds £2 billion a year, of which a high proportion may be caused by congestion.

9.   The biggest resource which is wasted by congestion is time. Time which is wasted and unproductively used in traffic jams can be valued in money terms. The figures which result are often very big. The most recent study quantifying these costs was undertaken by the British Road Federation (BRF). Total congestion costs in Greater London and the former metropolitan counties in 1987-88 amounted to an estimated £3168 million, of which about 72% (or £2280 million) represented the cost of non-working time wasted by congestion. If other large towns and cities are included as well the cost of congestion measured in this way might exceed £5000 million.

10.   The gross cost of congestion is the sum of all of these and might exceed £10,000 million in current prices.

Conclusion

11.   Road traffic congestion is a very costly phenomenon and is perceived by most road users as such. Congestion costs are difficult to calculate precisely because congestion is defined in a relative rather than absolute way and some of the assumptions which underlie estimates of the full costs of congestion are not realistic or generally attainable; this particularly applies to estimates of the cost of congestion in cities.

12.   Given these caveats, monetary quantification of the costs of congestion suggests that total costs to road users alone may exceed £10,000 million. Perhaps about half of this represents the money value of the adverse effects congestion has on the quality of life. Even if it proved impossible to evaluate congestion costs in money terms at

all, it would be impossible to deny the adverse effects which congestion has on the environment and ultimately the quality of peoples lives, especially if they live in cities. The qualitative as well as the quantitative costs of congestion are enormous and the realization of equivalently large benefits for the citizen and the life of the nation as a whole is conditional on the long term resolution of congestion.

Annex D. Access to airports and ports

Airports

1. Over the past decade activity at UK airports has increased dramatically with terminal passengers (arrivals and departures) rising from 46 million per annum to 86 million per annum and cargo rising from 705,000 tonnes per annum to 975,000 tonnes per annum. Of this traffic, however, around 40% of passengers and 59% of freight pass through Heathrow with 22% of passengers and 20% of freight passing through Gatwick. Manchester Airport accounts for 10% of passengers and 7% of freight.

2. The DTp estimates that passenger traffic will rise from 86 million per annum to 164-234 million per annum over the next 15 years, depending upon the strength of the economy. The share of the traffic at regional airports is projected to rise from 33% to more than 37% over the period. The passenger traffic increase will be partly met by the development of Stansted Airport which at present caters for only around 1 million passengers per annum.

Extent of the problem

3. It will be seen from the above figures that the bulk of the traffic arises at Heathrow, Gatwick and Manchester although traffic at Stansted will increase substantially over the next few years. Severe congestion occurs only at the approaches to Heathrow Airport where the adjacent sections of the M25 and the M4 provide some of the worst congestion problems of the entire motorway network. The introduction of the British Rail express rail service from Gatwick Airport to London has contained the development of congestion in the approaches to the airport and the planned express rail link from the centre of Manchester to the airport at Ringway should provide similar benefits to that airport. There are no severe congestion problems associated with the remaining UK airports.

Options for action

4. In July 1988 the Government approved a rail link from Heathrow to Paddington via a 6.5 km new line to connect the airport terminals with British Rail's Western Region main line. BAA is to meet around 80% of the cost. Trains will run at 15 minute intervals and the journey time to Paddington will be 16 minutes. This much needed rail link will contribute significantly to the containment of congestion around the airport but additional measures will prove necessary if future growth is to be accommodated. Improvements to the M25 and the M4 are planned and studies are in hand of other possible measures to relieve congestion in the area. There is a strong probability, however, that a new motorway linking Heathrow and Gatwick embracing junctions with the M40, M4, M3 and M23 will be needed, possibly together with a high speed rail link between the two airports, connected to the new high speed Channel Tunnel line.

5. There are reservations about the future for Stansted traffic. If the air traffic growth predictions prove to be correct it seems probable that traffic at Stansted could rise to 25 million terminal passengers per annum. The Stansted rail link will connect to the London – Cambridge main line which will be inadequate to cope with the resultant flow of rail passengers and Liverpool Street station will be unable to

accommodate the London bound traffic without severe congestion arising. It would be wise to study these possibilities further with a view to incorporating any necessary works (such as a St Pancras link) into the plans for London's railways which are currently under analysis.

Ports

6. Although at present there is no severe congestion along the access routes to our major ports this situation could deteriorate unless some of the south coast ports such as Dover, Tilbury and Portsmouth are provided with motorway standard links into the motorway system. Furthermore detailed examination of the road links to Felixstowe port should now encompass the probable traffic flows after the expansion of the port is complete. This may well be particularly relevant to the A12 London road.

7. The North East ports need an East Coast Motorway to assist their development and the North West ports which have relatively good road links, need a high speed freight rail link to the Channel Tunnel.

Annex E.   Local Association submissions

E1.   London Association

Problems

1.   London's problems are closely related to those of the wider south-eastern section of England and any solution must deal with this wider area.

2.   Congestion is serious because companies competing in Europe and other markets may decide to relocate in Peterborough or in the north of England or indeed other options such as France or Belgium. In particular financial institutions may with the advent of advanced information technology find it more cost-effective to concentrate their efforts in other cities.

3.   The issue of transport needs to be resolved if the country is to remain at least in its present position in world markets. If the nation is to make progress then radical changes are needed.

Causes

4.   A primary cause of congestion is the increasing tendency for people to live in dormitory or country areas while working within the conurbation. As relative affluence increases this is becoming a more feasible proposition to a greater number of people. This phenomenon has equal if not greater importance in causing congestion than the general prospect of land use planning.

The future

5.   There have been some contributions to a solution such as the Central London Rail Study but until such time as a full study is undertaken over a wider area no master plan can be designed. That area needs to include perhaps the whole of BR Network SouthEast in rail terms and an area which in road terms extends beyond the M25.

6.   With greater affluence and higher expectations of comfort the travelling public look upon public transport in quite a different way to earlier generations. Public transport, however quick, is compared to the comfort of a car journey and is not attractive enough to offer an irresistible alternative.

7.   Public transport needs a radical revision in terms of capacity, comfort, convenience and safety. This will not be achieved without considerable investment. Proposals put forward by the Government seek London local authority (LA) financial support for London Underground improvements. The population of the London boroughs may well benefit from an improved transport system but so will the population outside London. The most important factor is the viability of London as a commercial and financial centre in terms of the economic strength of the UK as a whole. London's transport system is of national concern and should be treated as such. Parliament needs to take responsibility for it now. To what degree financial assistance is required, and from whom, must be part of a wider debate.

8.   In addition to improvements in public transport to increase capacity, options which need detailed study as to their practicability and effectiveness are to

(a)   reduce in real terms the available off-street parking spaces in central London, both public and private

(b)   remove large quantities of on-street car parking (and increase road flow capacity as a by-product) and rigorously enforce no waiting regulations

(c)   adopt a policy which will provide cheap car parking at outer tube and rail stations to encourage modal change

(d)   encourage companies through the tax system to move to *carte orange* schemes (employer subsidized season tickets)

(e)   remove the company car from the renumeration package except where that vehicle is an essential tool of the job

(f)   consider road pricing only if all else fails.

9.   It is considered that increased public transport availability with positive discouragement of cars is the most likely combination to succeed and an appropriate organizational structure for London is therefore required.

Organizational structure for the future

10.   Since the 1950s there have been few policies adopted by central or London government that have been mutually consistent or agreed. There is a vital need for an organization to co-ordinate transport in London. Proposals to reconstitute a body in the likeness of the GLC can be dismissed since it failed to produce either an effective planning structure and/or a consistent or coherent transport policy.

11.   An intermediate proposal, a council made up of 32 borough elected members with participation of government departments and transport authorities (such as London Bus and London Underground) might be even less effective than the GLC, the DTp, the DoE have been in the past, given the large number and diversity of members.

12.   A more radical solution is considered necessary and the formation of a London metropolitan transport authority (LMTA) is recommended which would have the following characteristics.

(a)   It should be an independent body, not operated as part of a Department of State, but responsible only to Parliament. It should be non-political, non-elected, and should have as part of its membership representatives of interested bodies, such as Confederation of British Industry, the Association of London Authorities, and the London Boroughs Association, but these members should be lesser in number than nominated board members.

(b)   It should be able to raise its own capital, but would require substantial Government funds during, say, its first 10 years, to catch up in terms of capacity and safety requirements.

(c)   The area under LMTA control could be as wide as BR Network SouthEast in rail terms, the London Regional Transport area, and in road terms at least the area within M25.

(d)   It would be the strategic authority for the main road network, at least within the M25 and including all trunk roads and motorways, incorporating the functions of London Regional Office of DTp.

(e)   It would be the strategic authority in relation to all transport matters and would not act as operator, that would be undertaken by a reformed Network SouthEast, London Underground, and

London Buses. LAs would run their own local roads and act as agents for LMTA roads including main roads, trunk roads and motorways.

(f) The LMTA would be the primary advisor to the DoE (and thereby the LAs) on transport matters in relation to land use planning.

(g) LAs would produce their unitary plans following firm guidance notes for approval by the DoE, and the LMTA would be responsible for providing a proper and suitable transport system to match.

(h) The LMTA would, of right, advise on large planning applications or proposed new generators of traffic. LAs and the DoE would take account of the LMTA's views in relation to the potential premature nature of such applications. If however the application were approved, the LMTA would be obliged to respond to demand. It would have no power of direct refusal.

(i) Sponsors of new developments generating new traffic would be required to provide funds for use in general improvements to the transportation system, rather than specific improvements designed to serve the development.

Air travel

13. The Civil Aviation Authority forecast a doubling in air passenger numbers between 1987 and the year 2000. They have said that there is no case for taking artificial measures to stimulate growth of non-London airports at the expense of London airports, yet conclude that London area airports will need an additional runway by the year 2000 and advocate the extension of hours to include operations into what are now the quiet hours.

14. The environmental effect of late night flights make this extended operation unacceptable and increased numbers of passengers will have a severe impact on congestion.

15. The current emphasis appears to be one in which airport operators renounce any responsibility for their passengers beyond the airport boundary. There appears to be no consideration of the transport connections essential for the easy and effective dispersal of passengers. For example Heathrow adopts a drain principle whereby the vast majority of passengers are poured into the centre of London for transit on to the final destinations. This therefore means there are two focuses of passenger attention: one at Heathrow and the other at the centre of London. It is essential that this double handling of passengers is reduced significantly.

16. If for no other reason than safety, to allow unrestricted growth up to an absolute maximum of capacity of the London airports would not be the best option. Air space associated with the regional airports is likely to be safer and be able to absorb growth. It would be beneficial to encourage the development of regional airports, and this would need to be in the form of restraint of London's airports.

17. To direct air traffic away from London could result in certain traffic transferring to other European airports. This threat could well be real but it would seem that uncontrolled development of London's airports will place unacceptable demands on the transport infrastructure and local residents.

E2. South Eastern Association

Introduction

1.   The situation in the South East is one of extreme congestion in the movement of people for considerable periods of most days. This is true whether considering the movement of people to and from London, the more major towns such as Tonbridge Wells, Maidstone, or the Medway Towns, or even into the smaller towns. The congestion is seen as considerably extended journey times by road, overcrowding especially in trains, or a combination of both if travelling by bus. There is also serious congestion at peak holiday periods, especially so on the M25 at the Dartford Tunnel at all summer weekends.

2.   Congestion on the roads is a particular concern to the commercial interest of the region. Costs of delays due to overcrowded or inappropriate road systems, especially in port areas, are significant and likely to worsen. The effect of road repairs and accidents can be very serious indeed in terms of congestion and delay.

3.   The problems on the railways, with commuter traffic to London, are very pressing. The prospect of improvement through the construction of the Channel Tunnel rail link is welcomed. There is, however, a need for improving the consultation and communication processes if significant changes in rail usage or expansion are contemplated. The difficulties over the Channel Tunnel high-speed link are a good indicator of this and are seen to be the result of poor PR work by British Rail.

Social and environmental aspects

4.   Car ownership is becoming increasingly widespread and the affluent society of the South East aspires to a much greater degree of mobility than was considered the norm perhaps 20 years ago. Control of this factor by pricing of either ownership or use is perhaps worthy of consideration.

5.   It is vital that every consideration is given to maintaining and improving the environment of people's homes and of their working places and town centres. These objectives are difficult to achieve if road improvements or railways are to be built, but they are of paramount importance. The gain is doubtful if journey time is improved by two miles per hour at the expense of a large number of people's living conditions.

Solutions to the problem

6.   There is no overall solution, but there are ways to alleviate the problems. Considerable levels of investment will be needed and ways must be found of arriving at cost benefit figures which recognize the savings of costs of delays.

Railways

7.   Travel within the conurbations must be switched to alternative means of transport such as light railways or underground railways. LRT may be appropriate in linking the larger conurbations, for example between Maidstone and the Medway Towns.

8.   The proposed high speed link, with stations at Ashford and mid Kent (linking with an LRT system), will relieve pressure from elsewhere

including rail services from west Kent. There does not seem to be any prospect of an early improvement.

Roads

9.   It is only a temporary relief to increase the number of lanes on most trunk roads. Bottlenecks such as the two lane M20 (Maidstone bypass) are clearly exceptions. It is better to duplicate routes for example, two rings 5-10 miles inside and outside the M25.

10.   Congestion within major towns is almost exclusively self generated. Hence the need for light railways.

11.   It is essential that all urban developments whether road or LRT are not carried out in isolation. A broad land use transportation plan is needed.

12.   Smaller towns and villages may be improved by bypasses.

Ports

13.   There is a need for improvements on the A2 and A20 to connect Dover, the Medway crossings and the access, both road and rail, to Ramsgate.

E3. Southern Association

The problem

1.   Despite improvements to infrastructure and services, congestion is now seen by travellers as an in-built feature of transport especially at peak times and many of whom are captive to these times. Policies for action should be based on this fact and should seek to balance solutions against acceptable levels of congestion. Acceptable service levels could perhaps have been achieved on public transport. However, with roads it is open to question whether the environmental consequences of providing the required service might have been acceptable or achievable.

Solutions
Construction

2.   Past steps to provide for unlimited demand have proved to be inadequate. Studies should be undertaken to show the consequences of providing for unlimited demand and indeed the question should be posed as to whether providing for unlimited demand is desirable or indeed practical.

3.   Urban road building in general has not relieved problems and, although useful in some instances, is not the complete answer.

Modal change

4.   History shows that transferring travellers from road to rail only relieves road space for others attracted by the easier journey. Although the overall capacity of the road and transport system increases, road congestion soon reverts to its previous levels.

Traffic management

5.   Traffic management techniques by their very nature seek to facilitate traffic flow. Increased route speeds attract more traffic because the speed deterrent factor has been eased. Inevitably congestion will return not only because of the more attractive route but because of natural traffic growth.

6.   Current electronic systems such as urban traffic control and SCOOT are by no means widespread and even London is not yet covered by a complete SCOOT system. Furthermore such electronic tools as Autoguide and access control are not yet widely used and basic traffic management, such as banned turns, has not been rigidly employed on a comprehensive basis. On motorways, ramp metering might form part of a package of control measures.

Restraint

7.   Travellers who are frustrated by congestion, because it is seen to be insoluble, are more likely to accept forms of enforced traffic restraint such as electronic road pricing. Although this measure was not considered acceptable in the past because spare road capacity was available it is more likely to be politically acceptable now.

8.   Restricting car access for commuters can be achieved by pricing or other means. The released road will then be taken up by other users. Restriction of access by car, and therefore of personal freedom, may cause companies to move away from conurbations and thus hinder attempts to regenerate inner city areas.

9.   A further consequence of restraint is an additional stimulus to

encourage out of town and regional shopping centres and, in consequence, extra travel on the primary and secondary road networks. This whole problem must be considered part of an overall plan which co-ordinates development with the infrastructure capacity of the area.

Forecasting

10. Predicting traffic growth accurately has had a bad track record and additional research should be funded to find more reliable predictors of traffic. There needs to be a better understanding of generated traffic so that a more accurate estimate of it can be made.

11. Much reconstruction and maintenance is a direct result of an underestimate of HGV traffic growth, vehicle weights and overloading. Models should be developed to predict HGV growth more accurately and more checks made with the purpose of apprehending overweight vehicles with corresponding fines to match the severity of overloading.

Planning

12. The system of road planning and operating in this country is too restrictive and complex to encourage private enterprise. A different type of public inquiry system would be needed to expedite road planning. To construct large links in a reasonable timescale, public inquiry procedures must be changed and better compensation given to those affected.

Conclusion

13. Infrastructure investment should be such that a nation's economic needs are met while meeting most of the social needs as well. Investment planners should be mindful of the less well off in society who have transport and travel needs also. Nevertheless more money must be spent on developing and maintaining the means of communication and travel.

E4. Home Counties Association

General

1. Traffic conditions similar to those experienced in the peak hours are now accepted as normal in many parts of the Home Counties. If traffic flows are impeded further, total immobility will result. Some form of constraint or selectivity on vehicle use would seem to be inevitable simply to prevent this situation deteriorating.

2. More infrastructure in the South East of England is needed, but investment in non-road transportation systems will be necessary in many urban areas in the future where further extensive road building would be environmentally and politically unacceptable.

3. Local authorities need to have access to better quality regional forecasts when planning future transportation requirements. Government policy towards the use of capital allocations should be reviewed and there is a need for local authorities to be able to tap the private sector to fund necessary transportation improvements.

4. Government policy for highway provision is piecemeal and lacks a strategic framework. There needs to be a new long term look at transport needs (possibly with another Green Paper).

5. Planning of transportation provision needs to be integrated with local planning factors and land use policy.

Trunk road congestion

6. The most seriously congested sectors of the M25 are carrying 140,000 vehicles per weekday, and widening to dual four lanes is now in progress on some sections. The M1, M4 and M3 motorways are all suffering serious congestion at peak periods so that the provision of dual four lane construction is now under consideration for specified sections.

7. The M40 Oxford–Birmingham route is currently under construction over the whole of the outstanding length except for the dual three lane section between Waterstock and Wendlebury which is scheduled to be started in autumn 1989. The remaining dual two lane section at High Wycombe is also to be improved to dual three lanes to provide an overall dual three lane route through the whole of the Home Counties Association area by 1991, easing congestion in this busy corridor.

8. The A1(M) through Hertfordshire and Bedfordshire has long been utilized as an alternative route north to avoid the M1. The A41 through Hertfordshire, Buckinghamshire and Oxfordshire has serious congestion at peak periods in Kings Langley, Berkhamsted, Aylesbury, Bicester and Banbury – the only dual two lane sections available at the current time in the Home Counties area being the one mile bypass of Tring and the Watford bypass section north to the M25. The impending construction of the Bicester bypass will alleviate this situation to some extent but the subsequent completion of the Kings Langley–Berkhamsted–Aston Clinton bypass cannot be anticipated before the early to mid 1990s.

Berkshire

9. Development pressures have chronically overloaded Berkshire's road network. The county has the highest level of car ownership in the UK and car ownership is rising faster than the national average. Congestion is worsening, particularly in town centres, on approach roads to the centres and in locations with large concentrations of industrial and commercial development. The M4 and M25 in the county are both overloaded, and this overloading undermines their efficiency. These trends will certainly continue unless development in Berkshire can be eased. There is great concern about the quality of transport in the future.

10. While major conventional improvements to highways are essential, improvements on an environmentally acceptable scale cannot cope with forecast private vehicle movements. Serious consideration should be given to new forms of transport (for example, LRT in the central area of the county).

11. Berkshire is facing a growing funding gap to finance necessary road improvements. Block grant provision continues to decline relative to other counties. Transport supplementary grant provision is relatively unimportant and capital allocations are no higher than the average for other counties. It is highly unlikely that the county will be able to accommodate adequately the revenue consequences of the additional growth without a significant increase in the local rate burden. There is concern that central Government might in future take account of the contributions likely from developers when determining levels of capital expenditure.

Oxfordshire

12. A longer term strategic look at transport needs is required which should not rely on new road building to meet all travel demand. Instead, future transport policies should seek to reduce the need to travel by, amongst other things, integrating land use policies fully with transportation. There is a problem of increasing loading of traffic on minor county roads arising from the dispersal of jobs and population in the region. Big lorries should have restricted access to country roads.

Reading

13. Congestion in Reading has significantly worsened during the last 2-3 years. It has been calculated that on an average day 30,000 motorists are late for work each day, losing about 250,000 man hours each year at a cost calculated as £1,167,000. Businesses in Reading have reacted adversely to these costs.

14. Road improvements and traffic management schemes will have only short term benefits, however. The inner distribution road will not provide long term solutions to the traffic problems. Other solutions are needed in the longer term, of which bus travel may become significant. Provision of a better quality bus service and of more bus lanes is required. The local authority may need to put up the money for this by pump priming, and the necessary powers to do this already exist.

15. There is not a viable case for an LRT facility in Reading because of the absence of the necessary passenger volumes. Creation of park-and-ride facilities would not be justified given the absence of an outer ring road.

Oxford

16.   The main instrument available to Oxford City Council to deal with congestion is the balanced transport policy. Park-and-ride facilities have been provided and public transport has been encouraged in a deliberate policy of carrot and stick. Accidents rates have declined, the environment has been enhanced and accessibility to the city centre has increased without adding to traffic congestion.

17.   A significant start-up subsidy was required to get the park-and-ride scheme into operation, but by the early 1980s self-sufficiency had been obtained. Park-and-ride has become so well established in Oxford that private developers of sites in the city centre have been prepared to make financial contributions for additional parking spaces at park-and-ride sites.

Slough

18.   The overall traffic situation in Slough is not critical because of the relief offered by the M4 motorway and the layout of the town itself. In accident situations on the M4, diversions along the A4 through the towns occur virtually bringing it to a standstill. Thus, the primary roads (for example the A4) through the area need to be improved. The policy is to provide new developments with access by car. The geography of Slough is not compatible with park-and-ride schemes. Since 1986-87 Slough has had a policy of charging all new developments for a share in the projected traffic improvements. The improvements are then instituted as funds permit.

Guildford

19.   The main problem in Guildford is insufficient provision for car parking. Very high costs to industry resulting from insufficient road capacity (for example on the M25) were noted.

Bedford

20.   Traffic levels have reached saturation point in peak periods. The A428 Bedford bypass is included in the national preparation programme but will not be available to provide any short term relief.

Luton

21.   Luton suffers peak hour congestion problems, aggravated by late night shopping on specified days. Planned relief roads will not improve the situation for some years and future commercial and residential developments might negate any benefits.

22.   Increased use of public transport may relieve the traffic situation provided that some form of limitation is imposed on the use of private transport. In some town centre locations, public transport currently causes obstruction generating congestion.

Aylesbury

23.   The partly completed ring road provides some relief but congestion is still manifested at peak periods. A number of long distance bus and coach routes pass through the town outside peak hours but do not contribute significantly to congestion.

British Rail

24.   Network SouthEast commuter traffic into London is expected to grow by 25% on average over the whole of the region, but higher levels of growth (35-40%) are anticipated in the Thames, Chiltern and south-western sectors. These growth rates are based on the 220,000-300,000 additional jobs expected in Central London from developments including Canary Wharf, King's Cross, Broadgate and Spitalfields. Growth in longer distance commuting has increased rapidly in the past few years. New rolling stock is planned for introduction into service

in the early 1990s which could provide improved standing room and greater seating capacity.

Luton Airport

25.   Luton International Airport has a terminal capacity of 3.5 million passengers per annum and a throughput of 2 million passengers per annum, and although the airport capacity could be increased to 5 million passengers per annum, this would be the absolute limit due to other and air traffic control constraints. The UK total passenger movement is approximately 90 million passengers per annum so that Luton's proportion could ultimately represent almost 6% of the market.

E5. East Anglian Association

1. The East Anglian Association covers the four counties of Norfolk, Suffolk, Essex and Cambridgeshire. Traditionally East Anglia has been thought of as the "granary of England" with a landscape of arable agriculture, a sparse population widely distributed in small historic towns and villages, and a coastline varying from seaside to salt marshes. In reality, it is the fastest growing region in the country, with the lowest regional unemployment rate and the fastest growing population.

2. Because of the booming local economy, including high technology in the Cambridgeshire area, thriving tourism, the expanding container port of Felixstowe, Stansted airport, and the Sizewell B nuclear power stations, signs of congestion are already apparent. The Eastern Region Primary Route Network Review 1988 concludes that the region's roads are more densely trafficked than the national average, and that traffic is continuing to grow at a rate about half as high again as the national average. Expenditure monitoring shows that despite some slippage during the years 1987-88, expenditure on motorways and trunk roads kept ahead of the estimated needs to 2006, but expenditure on county council primary roads fell short over the five year period 1984-88. The Channel Tunnel and the political consequences of 1992 are almost certain to contribute to road, rail and air transport problems.

3. In order to produce some quantitative measure of congestion in urban areas, and provide a basis for comparisons between different locations now with variations over time, a survey was undertaken in the cities of Norwich, Chelmsford and Cambridge. Journeys into the town centre during the morning rush hour were timed, and the build-up of traffic night and morning were counted. A traffic count into Chelmsford showed a rapid flow build-up from 100 vehicles/hour at 6.00 am to 1300 vehicles/hour at the peak time of 9.00 am. Similar conditions were reflected in Cambridge, where average speed on radial roads varied from 27.9 mph (7.30-8.00), 18.1 mph (8.00-8.30) and 11.4 mph between 8.30 and 9.00 am. The results showed some correlation between peak flows and the delays recorded during specific half-hour periods. It was also apparent that drivers on regular routes had come to accept a certain amount of delay, and only became aware of a hold-up when journey times were excessive.

4. Thus continuing and increasing expenditure on the transport infrastructure will be required, merely to maintain the present situation. The up-grading of roads, provision of bypasses, and alternative networks may all be required to play a part in improving inter-urban communications. To relieve urban congestion, all forms of traffic management must be explored including pedestrianization, park-and-ride, improved public transport, out of town shopping precincts, provision for cyclists. These various experiments need to get past the research and development stage before the problems become chronic.

5. Ultimately, pure engineering solutions will reach their limit, at least in urban areas, and political decisions will be required to restrain demand by some form of pricing, that is licensing, taxation or rationing.

E6. South Wales Association

1.   Since the establishment of the Welsh Office in 1964 the considerable investment on the primary, trunk and motorway network has brought the Welsh highway system into the 20th century, but the rapid industrial expansion, particularly in South Wales, has resulted in traffic increases above the national average and its attendant problems of increased congestion.

2.   This increased prosperity has enabled people working in urban areas to migrate to rural areas to live. For example, the Vale of Glamorgan to the west of Cardiff has increased its population by 8.2% in the last six years compared with 0.8% for all Wales. Commuter journeys have increased accordingly.

3.   Although unemployment is above the average for Great Britain it has fallen 4.3% to 12.5% in the last two years compared with the national average decrease of 3.6% to 9.2%.

4.   These factors, with perhaps others, have contributed to an increase in car ownership over the last five years of 14.1% (18.6% in the South Glamorgan-Cardiff area) compared with an average over the whole of Great Britain of 12.3% and indications are that this trend will accelerate in the future.

5.   Although the per capita GDP in Wales is below the UK average it is increasing at a faster rate. During three years it has increased from 85.3% of the UK average to 87.1%.

6.   The continuation of the rapid economic growth in South Wales relies heavily on the free flow of people, raw materials and manufactured goods both within the area and to other population centres within the UK and abroad. The greater distances of South Wales from many other centres emphasizes this need as journey time is perhaps more important than distance in transportation terms.

7.   This need for access to England and beyond is one of the reasons for the urgent need to provide a second road crossing of the River Severn and also provides a case for the removal of the existing tolls. A survey in 1983 indicated that under normal conditions (that is, not restricted by accidents or high winds) the cost of delays at the toll booths including loss of time and extra vehicle operating costs was over £1 million in addition to the tolls. The cost of collecting tolls was £0.5 million and together these accounted for half the toll revenue of £3 million which by any standards cannot be regarded as an efficient or economically sound operation.

8.   Within South Wales itself proposals to alleviate some major congestion trouble spots, particularly on the M4, are either programmed (Brynglas Tunnels by Newport now operating at 16% above the recommended maximum flows, and the missing link of the M4 west of Swansea) or being considered (the duplication of the M4) and these should give some relief in the short and medium term respectively.

However, the adequacy of these proposals must be considered in the light of future developments quite apart from the current growth in the industrial economy. These include among others the Cardiff Bay development and the rapid expansion of tourism in the area.

9.   The Cardiff Bay development alone is forecast to generate 250,000 trips a day. This compares with the 1,000,000 trips a day currently generated in the whole of South Glamorgan and makes no allowance for normal growth.

10.   The decline of heavy industry in South Wales has released considerable areas of land, many of which have been reclaimed and developed, some for industry and commerce but much for tourism and leisure purposes, particularly along the coast from Newport with its proposed River Usk barrage and riverside developments, to Swansea with its marina and associated complex, and on to Llanelli with its country park, wildfowl trust, motor racing circuit and other leisure facilities.

11.   Inland, Newport's Tredegar House and Park, Islwyn's linear country park, the Ebbw Vale's 1992 garden festival site and the Big Pit industrial museum are but a few of the tourist attractions developed in the region apart from the Black Mountains and Brecon Beacons which are being provided with increased facilities for the more energetic visitors.

12.   The expansion of tourism will not only increase traffic generally but create heavy flows particularly during holiday months and at weekends.

13.   This increased emphasis on tourism together with the rapid industrial expansion of the region calls for an urgent reassessment of future traffic volumes to include, in addition to normal growth, the effect of redistributed and generated traffic. Due to the mountainous nature of the terrain there are restraints both on the routeing of new highways and the improvement of existing ones but, in general, sufficient is available for both these purposes. However, with the increasing development, decisions must be made at an early stage on land requirements for transportation purposes.

14.   In the conurbations, in a large majority of cases, the only available way of increasing road capacity is by the implementation of more rigorous traffic management measures.

15.   As elsewhere in the UK, Wales suffers from delays caused by the operation of the public utilities and also highway and bridge maintenance, although the latter cause will decrease to some degree due to the emphasis being put on whole life costing.

16.   The use of buses has decreased. During the last four years the 236 million trips a year for all Wales has decreased by 17% and there is no reason to suppose that South Wales differs from the Welsh average or that this decline will not continue.

17.   The commuter rail routes, particularly in South Glamorgan (the Cardiff catchment area) have been developed over the last four years

and, although they do not make a very significant impact on the overall transportation scene, there is potential for further development.

18.   In the western section of the industrial region, particularly West Glamorgan, emphasis has been placed on the provision and improvement of strategic road corridors to obtain the maximum benefit from the motorway and trunk road network.

19.   The Cardiff/Wales Airport serves the region well and has excellent access from the M4 motorway. Although there has been an extensive programme of development and improvement over the past years, further development, particularly to encourage scheduled services and air cargo movements, would establish it more firmly as a regional airport thus making a greater contribution to the economy of South Wales as well as, to some degree, relieving the pressure on the London airports.

20.   In order to ensure the continuation of the economic growth of South Wales in the most efficient way it is essential that an integrated transport plan be drawn up to ensure that the most effective use is made of available resources.

21.   The solution to the problems of highway congestion cannot be merely to build more roads as this is, particularly in urban areas, environmentally and economically impossible for all practical purposes, and would further detract from the existing public services. The plan must encourage the expansion of mass transportation systems and attract the travelling public to use them by providing reliable and frequent services with good terminal facilities, including car parks to encourage park-and-ride. This applies particularly in the Glamorgans and to some degree in Gwent.

22.   As in other parts of the UK, congestion will not be cured, only contained or to some extent reduced. The attraction of the travelling public to mass transportation systems is preferable to legal or fiscal restraints such as limited access or road pricing with their costly problems of enforcement. It may, however, be necessary to revert to these latter methods to some degree to encourage (or force) commuters to use public transport.

23.   Wales is fortunate in operating under a single, well co-ordinated government department, the Welsh Office, which must ensure that delays in administrative procedures are kept to a minimum in the planning and implementation of transportation projects.

24.   The congestion problems in South Wales are not limited to the improvement of transportation systems within the principality and the provision of a second crossing of the River Severn. In common with other areas of Great Britain there is considerable concern that the lack of adequate road and rail links around London to give access to the Channel Tunnel for both manufactured goods and passengers will have an inhibiting effect on exporting goods to the Continent. It will be of no assistance to the economic prosperity of Wales if the 2-3 hours to cover the 150-200 miles to London merely ends in uncontrolled and uncontrollable congestion on the western edge of the metropolis.

E7. North Western Association

The problem

1. Congestion is a symptom of the failure to develop the transportation system to meet the needs of commerce and society. It results from a failure to recognize the nature and importance of transport and to plan and implement the necessary improvements. Some criticism for this has been levelled, unfairly, at transportation planners.

2. Even in the areas where comprehensive land use and transportation plans were produced, the transport proposals have not been fully implemented and as a consequence congestion remains a problem. Nationwide, investment in infrastructure has failed to keep pace with investment in vehicles and their use.

3. These problems have been exacerbated by the failure of governmental, administrative and professional organizations to reflect the multifaceted nature of transport and its central role in an advanced and developed society.

The North West view

4. The North West is a region of remarkable diversity and contrast. The population of almost 7 million makes North West England and the second largest region in Britain. Its workforce contributes more to the national economy than any other region except South East England and it accounts for about one tenth of the GDP and one eighth of the nation's manufacturing output.

Channel Tunnel rail link

5. To enable the region to benefit fully from the opportunities provided by the Single European Market it is considered that provision of direct access to the Channel Tunnel and the development of more direct services from North West airports are necessary to cater for travel between the region and mainland Europe. This will also make a modest contribution towards easing some of the congestion problems in the South East.

Roads

6. There is pressing need to speed up investment in the highway network in the region. The network as a whole is faced with safety, environmental and congestion problems. It is essential that these problems are addressed now to assist economic growth in both the heavily populated and the more remote parts of the region. Many lengths of the national motorway network in the North West will be overloaded by the turn of the century despite the proposals in the latest White Paper *Roads for prosperity*.

Rail

7. Overcrowding on trains in the region has become a problem on certain local and long distance services at peak times. There are some rail routes where line congestion is a problem, such as on the section between Manchester Piccadilly and the Windsor Link, but line capacity problems are not widespread in the North West.

8. There are significant opportunities for easing the problems of highway congestion, particularly in large urban areas, by developing the rail system (for example improved and additional services, extension

of electrification, new stations) an approach which has been successfully pursued in Merseyside or by developing Light Rail Transit which is being pursued in Manchester. Such investment is constrained by the grant criteria currently adopted by the DTp.

9. Support for the above views and for many of the recommendations below can be found in reports from a wide variety of organizations in the North West. As an example of this the following quotation is cited from the North West Region CBI report *Towards 2000 - transport and the North West*

> "Britain urgently needs to invest more in infrastructure to match the growth of the economy. Good communications are vitally important for the business community and the consumer. Congestion costs money. In the case of roads, an extra £3 billion per annum. Better road and rail services are required to ensure the North West can reap the real benefits of the Channel Tunnel link. We must make better use of our port facilities, while further expansion at Manchester and Liverpool Airports is absolutely essential if the North West is to continue to grow and prosper."

The way forward

10. It is important to recognize that the transport of people or goods is not usually an end in itself, rather it is the means without which most activities could not function effectively. Congestion has implications on the economy of the country, on its businesses, and on the lives of its people. It is recommended that Government ensures the development and operation of an effective, efficient and economic total transportation system to meet the social and economic needs of the country.

Co-ordination and competition

11. In order to get the best out of the transport system it is necessary to spread the demands across the system with each mode catering for those movements for which it is best suited.

12. A common financial, economic and environmental framework should be introduced within which decision making on investment in the different modes of transport would accord to a set of mutually compatible criteria.

13. The fiscal and administrative regimes within which the different modes of transport operate should be adjusted so that their operation and use are subject to a common economic discipline, so that competition between operators and between modes leads not only to efficiency within each mode of transport but to an effective use of the transport system as a whole.

14. Freedom to travel around and to undertake one's activities with an increasing degree of choice can validly be regarded as a part of increasing prosperity and an improved quality of life. However, particularly during the next decade, it is unrealistic to expect that all parts of the transport system will be able to provide for all the demands made on it at all times of the day. What is required therefore is not some planned or prescribed pattern of activities with an idealized transport system to serve it; rather individual choice should be mobilized as a mechanism for promoting efficiency and reducing

congestion. Advances in information technology, driver and public transport user information systems, and in flexible employment arrangements all have contributions to make; some in the short term, others other the next ten to fifteen years.

15. Significant increases in the capacity of the transport system, by whatever means, and substantial shifts in the pattern of travel demand will inevitably take time to achieve. Meanwhile, much can be done to improve the present situation, to manage the existing transport systems more effectively and to reduce the damaging effects of breakdowns and maintenance operations.

Car parking and congestion

16. As well as the scope that the management of car parking can provide to relieve congestion directly, the use of information technology can integrate route choice and parking decisions to enable people to decide their time and destination of travel so as to reduce congestion further. Recently developed techniques may enable the maintenance or expansion of public parking in town centres, yet freeing the roads from parking search traffic and parking queues.

17. Major roads, and in urban areas important secondary routes, often provide the right-of-way for a multiplicity of underground utilities as well as acting as traffic arteries. Such utilities frequently require repair maintenance or replacement, inevitably requiring some occupation of road space where the resultant reduction in capacity can lead to significant traffic congestion. These roadworks are additional to those associated with the maintenance of the highway system itself. Emergency road closures or restrictions are unavoidable, but better use of information technology could mitigate their congestion effects. Non-emergency situations should be effectively co-ordinated to minimize traffic disruption. In order to obtain the optimum choice of construction or maintenance method, working practices, and road space occupied, procedures such as road space rental should be adopted.

Forecasts

18. Travel forecasting must be considered over a long timescale. The two factors which have the greatest influence on the amount of travel are changes in population and the state of the economy.

Conclusion

19. It is necessary to

(a) assess the long term requirements for movement
(b) determine the extent to which these requirements can be met and how rationing can be best effected
(c) establish a framework for the development and management of the total transport system
(d) develop the mechanisms for financing and control which ensure the efficient use of the system as a whole.

20. The implications of congestion are almost impossible to cost, although such costs are likely to be far in excess of the readily quantifiable elements such as the cost of delays. It is important that the financing of transport is put on a basis which reflects what is required of the transport system and the extent to which those needs are being met. It is essential that there is a comparable basis of evaluation for each type of proposal. From such an approach the overall priority of each a problem may be determined.

E8. Midlands Association

Congestion

1. Congestion is a long established problem of urban transportation and will continue into the foreseeable future. Over the past decade the problems of congestion have worsened, on all transport modes, to become an issue of great public concern.

Underprovision of infrastructure

2. Weaknesses in available data and often the neglect of generated traffic hinder the process of the accurate forecasting of demand which underpins transport provision, especially roads. The resulting underprovision is sometimes reflected in inadequate design criteria for roads which can lead either to premature deterioration of the structure or to the need for widening soon after initial completion. Both of these cause disruption and expense to road users. The provision of motorways is less in the UK than in many other big industrial countries. Selection criteria for new transportation schemes must take into account industrial and economic need. A review of planning and implementation procedures is needed in view of lengthy delays at the pre-construction stage.

Traffic restraint

3. On account of these delays, new construction is not an immediate option for tackling congestion. Instead, recourse must be had to methods of restraining demand and traffic management. Demand can be restrained in a number of ways ranging from flexi-time to road pricing. Such processes do need to be encouraged, possibly by Government legislation.

Statutory undertakers

4. Government needs to provide an appropriate legislative framework to encourage the statutory undertakers to minimize disruption they cause to motorists by possession and excavation of the road surface. Such activity is a frequent source of congestion. There has been progress so far in reviewing the activities of public utilities in this area, but Government might consider the benefits of applying the principle of lane rentals to statutory undertakers as a direct incentive for them to minimize delay and disruption. Overall, a new approach to the management of road space is needed so that the interests of road users are paramount.

Need for integration

5. Transportation needs vary greatly depending upon the scenario and type of transport required. Urban areas commonly have the most complex transport requirements and effective provision for them needs to be integrated so that transport modes are not treated in isolation from one another. More attention in the future needs to be paid towards interchange between the various modes of travel, such as the provision of park-and-ride schemes stemming from the development of ring roads and motorway boxes. Transportation investment programmes should be drawn up for conurbations to identify priorities and strategies. Groups of local authorities working with the regional offices of the DTp could achieve this.

Private investment

6. Private sector involvement in the financing of new transportation infrastructure raises three issues. First, schemes acceptable to the community, and giving a high rate of social return, are unlikely to be

acceptable to private investors, whose priority is to maximize private returns instead. Second, in view of the large risks involved, Government must work with the private sector to minimize uncertainty (for example in areas crucial for investment evaluation like traffic forecasts). Third, the recent commitment by Government to relax the rules governing the use of private finance in infrastructure projects needs to be clarified.

E9. Yorkshire Association

Problems

1.   In almost every aspect of transport there are signs of increasing congestion: aviation, public transport (particularly commuter rail services) and especially on the highway system. The impact is now significant in the larger urban areas, certain strategic routes such as the A1 and M62, and locations subject to peak holiday traffic. Congestion is spreading to affect more locations and for longer periods. It is clear that much of the urban road system is on a knife-edge at peak periods. Incidents such as an accident, breakdown, or loss of computer control of signals immediately result in very long queues which take a long time to clear. Focal points in the network such as main radials, inner ring roads, bridges, and tunnels are particularly vulnerable.

Rat-running

2.   Two aspects of the travelling public's reactions to congestion can readily be identified: an increase in the amount of rat-running and a spreading of the peak periods. A study of the A660 urban corridor in Leeds showed that between 1982-86 traffic flows on the A660 corridor increased by 13.7% over 16 hours compared with 14.5% in the sector as a whole, but in the morning and evening peaks there had been no increase, compared with 20% and 13% respectively in the sector overall. The corridor is running at capacity in the peaks and traffic has diverted, using more rat-runs in the process. Accident levels had increased in the A660 corridor compared with the rest of Leeds district where there was a reduction. A slight increase in noise levels had occurred on the secondary network.

Peak-spreading

3.   People are trying to avoid peak period travel. This is helped, in the urban areas in particular, by flexi-working. Fig. 4 shows the traffic flow profiles on the A1 near Wetherby (rural) for 1981-88. The filling up of the trough between the peaks is very pronounced and the histogram illustrates clearly the large increases before the morning peak and after the evening peak as the flow profile becomes longer and more of a plateau.

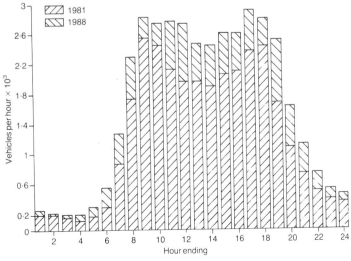

Fig. 4.   Traffic flow profiles on the A1 near Wetherby for 1981-88

Public transport

4. Another aspect of the problem of urban highway congestion is the effect on bus services. Bus operators consider that congestion has worsened considerably in recent years. Peak hour congestion in the larger urban areas regularly adds 33% to off-peak journey times. As a result additional running time has had to be built into bus timetables for Leeds in particular.

Suggested solutions
Highways

5. There is a continuing need for public investment on targeted highway improvements and certain new routes. New schemes are relatively more expensive, in part due to the increased emphasis rightly given to environmental considerations. The scope for private sector investment is believed to be restricted but contributions from developers under Section 52 of the Town and Country Planning Act 1971 or similar planning gain can prove valuable in specific cases.

Traffic management

6. Considerable benefits have already been achieved but there is still scope for more and for innovation. More sophisticated computer control of traffic signals and direction signs, including signs to car parks, developments such as Autoguide, tidal flow schemes, lanes reserved for multi-occupancy vehicles and ramp metering may each be implemented where appropriate. It is essential that highways are used to their optimum, and better enforcement of waiting restrictions is required. In Washington USA, the City has taken over enforcement from the police with a resulting reduction of 70-90% in parking offenses. Their scheme is self-financing and this option should be considered for the UK.

Public transport

7. Good public transport can have an impact on highway flows and congestion particularly in the long term reduction in the rate of traffic growth that would otherwise take place. There is a need for both public and private investment in public transport improvement and innovation. New systems, such as LRT, can prove particularly effective in attracting patronage and reducing congestion. The criteria for receiving grant under Section 56 of the Transport Act 1968 should be reviewed to make them more equitable in relation to highway grants by allowing more weight to be attached to user benefits.

Demand management

8. Positive restriction such as cordon pricing or road pricing are seen as inequitable and disliked by most motorists and politicians. These are seen as appropriate only in extreme cases and as some way in the future. Control over car parking, for long stay parking in particular, is an important factor in tackling congestion. Typically in a large urban centre 50% of long stay parking is private non-residential (PNR) over which the local authority has no control. To reduce the increase in congestion it is important to control the increase in new PNR spaces but it is recognized that in the inter-city competition for employment and prestigious town centre development the relaxation of parking restrictions can be a major incentive.

Other measures

9. Evidence has been submitted to illustrate ways in which the travelling public are spreading their journeys and using rat-runs more. This seems to be accompanied by a gradual adaptation to the level of congestion that it tolerated. Increased opportunities for flexible working should be encouraged. Developments in the field of information technology are also allowing more flexibility in the time of trips and giving some people greater freedom in planning their daily

and weekly pattern of trip making. A number of authorities have estimated that by the early years of the next century, between one third and one half of all work could be undertaken remotely.

Conclusion

10. There is no simple panacea but road traffic is increasing at about 5% per annum and action is required on a number of fronts to try to temper and accommodate future growth. Changes in legislation, such as bus de-regulation in the Transport Act 1985 and the loss of the powers of direction by highway authorities, coupled with increased acceptance of market forces, make it now more difficult to co-ordinate transport policies and the interaction of land use and transport. Improved collaboration is required between the various transport and planning agencies to ensure the most cost-effective use of resources to tackle the problem of congestion.

E10. Northern Counties

1. Factors adding to the growth of congestion include

(a) increased growth in income with a consequent growth in personal transport

(b) the spread of residences into suburban and semi-rural areas to escape from urban dereliction or to obtain something more affordable

(c) the increases in journey to work distances consequent upon the closure of local industries such as mining, shipbuilding and heavy mechanical engineering with the need to travel further afield to obtain employment, mainly in city centres

(d) the continuing switch to the transport of goods by road.

Main roads

2. The Northern Counties are reliant on roads to the South which are inadequate. The efficiency and safety of the A1 is compromised by a multiplicity of at-grade crossings and poor alignment. The A1 should be upgraded to motorway standards.

3. There is a need for a motorway link north of the current M1 termination near Leeds to the A1. Furthermore since congestion is growing on the M1 and A1, the examination of the feasibility of providing an East Coast Motorway linking the A19 at Teeside to the M11 via the Humber Bridge with enhancement of the M25 as a route to the South East and Channel Tunnel is becoming a matter of urgency and should be undertaken by the DTp.

4. The reliance on private sector funding for the East Coast Motorway is wholly inconsistent with any reasonable regional policy. Delay in construction will lead to the loss of markets to others who are more favourably placed, for example the French and Belgians.

5. Trunk roads which are in need of up-grading to dual carriageway standards with appropriate alignments include, the A1 Newcastle to Edinburgh route and the major east-west routes A66 and A69. These roads are frequently obstructed by congestion and accidents at single carriageway sections.

Urban congestion

6. The Tyne Bridge, which links two major junctions on the Newcastle and Gateshead sides of the river presents a serious congestion problem. Although a four lane highway it is saturated with traffic and queuing occurs which blocks exits both south and northbound, and obstructs access to the riverside regeneration sites.

7. There are a number of measures in hand which will ease the problem, however the only facility east of the Tyne Bridge is the Tyne Tunnel, a single two lane carriageway and this is heavily congested.

8. There is a vital need for regeneration in the Newcastle area to solve problems of unemployment but the traffic created can be predicted. The Newcastle area needs both regenerative works and new facilities to accommodate the traffic produced.

Channel Tunnel

9.   For journeys exceeding 300 km the transfer of goods by rail becomes viable. The construction of the Channel Tunnel therefore is an opportunity to reduce the amount of freight carried by road. The size of the Channel Tunnel freight trains, up to 1600 tonnes gross and 750 m in length, probably means that no single manufacturer in the North with the exception of ICI, British Steel or Nissan could assemble complete train loads. Suitable transhipment depots should be established in the regions: such as Tyne, Tees and an intermediate location, and one in the proximity of Carlisle in the west of the region.

10.   The directness of the route and the minimization of time lost in train assembly and clearing customs examination will be very relevant to the efficiency of operations. There is therefore a need for a direct route to the Tunnel to be located to the east of London so that the congested lines and junctions within London do not have to be utilized.

11.   The provision of dedicated freight lines around London will ease congestion on the M25 and other routes, and will aid regional growth by preserving and expanding the opportunities of regionally located manufacturers. It is essential that Section 42 of the Channel Tunnel Act should be repealed to enable the creation of national express links to the Channel Tunnel from the Northern Region, North West Region and Scotland so that they can be given a fair chance to compete in European markets.

Road pricing

12.   While there may be common acceptance of the need for restraint upon the use of the car, the degree to which road pricing or equivalent mechanisms can be used to counter congestion in areas in need of urban renewal and economic regeneration is probably very small.

13.   An enhanced public transport provision to offset reduced opportunities for private motoring is probably desirable. Essentially it is a matter to be decided by the policy and actions of central Government rather than free market forces whose actions will always be reactive rather than pro-active.

E11. Edinburgh and East of Scotland Association
Glasgow and West of Scotland Association

1.   Though no major congestion problems are currently experienced outside the urban areas, in the foreseeable future catastrophic failures in the movement of traffic are foreseen on certain of the single carriageway roads. These roads, designed on average annual traffic figures do not take into account the 3-4 month summer peaks, which are aggravated by an increasingly aggressive tourist industry. Vehicle breakdowns and emergency road works would greatly exacerbate such congestions; the position must be recognized, and the necessary works carried out before congestion becomes unacceptable.

2.   The SDD, in an endeavour to reduce the congestion resulting from roadworks on motorways and trunk roads, has recently successfully adopted lane rental schemes. A new specification for road design provides for an improved quality of road construction, with increased pavement depth, embodies whole life costing which evaluates delays due to construction and future maintenance, and provides for a 40 year life expectancy; these measures are intended to reduce the time taken for maintenance works and also their frequency. The strengthening of hard shoulders, existing and proposed, to be used as a spare lane is being investigated, as is the closing down of road repair works in the summer months.

Channel Tunnel

3.   The construction of the Channel Tunnel will provide a major opportunity for rail transport. To attract custom from the roads to the railways, the electrification of the main East Coast Line should be continued north of Edinburgh to Aberdeen. In addition a direct high speed service from the North to the Tunnel is required, bypassing the London blockage and providing a through route to European markets. So that industry and commerce in the North can benefit from the Tunnel, a direct fast through freight line from Glasgow to the Tunnel terminal is required, bypassing London.

4.   The congestion in the motorway network, particularly in the Midlands and South East, is of major concern to the long distance road user, commercial or private, and gives rise to fears that the benefits from the Tunnel and European markets, will be severely diminished as one moves North. A major north-south route is essential, including a new or enhanced road link round London, and an additional Thames crossing.

Edinburgh and East of Scotland

5.   Congestion points of the future should be identified at an early stage to allow remedial measures to be implemented in good time. Solutions to deal with present and future problems do exist and correct solutions are not hard to identify; the problem is one of finance. With only a fraction of the total vehicle and fuel taxes being spent on roads, a direct transport tax with the money collected being spent on a co-ordinated transport plan would tackle congestion in a positive way. It is not considered that road pricing would be an effective answer to urban congestion.

6.   Scotland has more growth potential than, say, the already

overgrown South East. This is particularly so in the congestion problems which could arise with the expanding tourist industry, which could reach serious dimensions particularly on the single track roads in the Highlands.

Short term options

7. Staggered working hours to avoid peak hour traffic rushes (for example flexi-time), an increased staggering of bank holidays and local holidays, the closing up of road maintenance work over holiday weekends, and the encouraging of package holiday firms to organize mid-week to mid-week holidays in an effort to avoid weekend rail and air traffic delays, are all options which would assist in relieving congestion.

Bus deregulation

8. Since deregulation of the buses, the public appears to have gained from greater competition, operators having to cut costs, and from a better service. However there are still too many buses competing for fewer passengers, the mini bus every half minute having taken over from the double-decker every five minutes. This has resulted in increasing congestion problems in urban areas. The situation is not as yet stable, with many new operators testing the market. Once the competition has settled down any problem due to congestion from de-regulation should disappear.

Rail electrification north of Edinburgh

9. BR have, on the basis of the economic assessment methods which are heavily biased against rail compared to roads, at the present time concluded that the electrification of the main line north of Edinburgh is not justified. If the present method of economic assessment, and the principle that individual modes of transport must stand on their own, are accepted, this might make sense. However, if the rail system is to be considered as part of a co-ordinated transportation system for the whole country, then the extension of the electrification is justified.

Co-ordination of transport policy

10. It could be argued that the road system competes unfairly with other transport modes, one result being road congestion. The vast network is readily available for the price of the motor tax; other transport modes cannot compete with the mobility of roads and have difficulty competing with the cost. To ease congestion, the users of the transportation system have to be efficiently spread around the various modes by means of a co-ordinated transport policy; this would be in the interests of the nation's economy, and also safety on the roads, rail and the air.

11. There are many examples of very successful local transportation co-ordination such as courier or post bus services in rural areas, and in urban areas interlocking road-rail systems with bus and rail timetables co-ordinated, railway stations carrying connecting bus timetables, bus stations with connecting rail timetables, car parking facilities provided by the road authorities at rail stations and so on.

Glasgow and West of Scotland

12. The congestion problems considered are centred on the Glasgow conurbation where the problems of congestion on inter-urban roads and motorways were dealt with, and considerable relief obtained, by measures taken over the past 25 years. Glasgow's comprehensive road-rail transportation plan of the early 1960s was substantially implemented as far as road construction was concerned over the first 15 years of its programme. This was designed to eliminate serious

congestion and improve the environment by keeping road construction ahead of traffic growth. As each section of the project was opened the predicted immediate benefits were noted. Pedestrianization schemes were implemented in formerly busy through city streets, traffic reduced dramatically on parallel radial routes with consequent reduction in noise and improvement in amenity, access to the city centre improved goods distribution, and new commercial development took place along the motorway corridor.

13. Congestion is occurring once again in certain areas due to the original intentions not being fully realized in recent years. The reasons for subsequent stages of the original highways plan not being implemented include capital expenditure restraint, planning delays, and a growing anti-motorway lobby due to complacency with the satisfactory situation which existed in the years following the completion of the first stages.

14. In recent years improvement of traffic conditions within the existing road framework have included the centrally integrated traffic control (CITRAC) project with its three phases – motorway control and surveillance; ramp control and diversion routeing: and urban traffic control. Major traffic management schemes have been undertaken including junction improvements on radial routes, and a system of one-way traffic routes in the city centre. Peak period commuting to the city centre is directly influenced by the central area parking policy which is aimed at discouraging commuting by car. Road pricing is likely to be politically unacceptable and could be impracticable in engineering terms.

15. Bus deregulation had an immediate effect of increased congestion. The situation now is less obvious and studies are in hand to assess the impact, though it is in the outlying areas where local congestion is most evident and continues to be so.

16. Two examples of alternative methods of dealing with congestion and improving capacity which have been implemented are a traffic management measure and a road infrastructure improvement. In both cases extensive before and after studies were undertaken to validate the work, and measures applied that were common were the application of control strategy and innovative modelling techniques. TRANSYT, a traffic signal modelling procedure was chosen, which accommodated variations in traffic volume, bus schedules, parking, turning volumes, cruise time, lane usage and width, location of parked cars. The base model was amended to include separate fuel consumption calculations, total network resource cost, an improved optimization method, and variations on the relevant emphasis within the model.

Aikenhead Road - radial route

17. Motorists were deliberately avoiding this route as poor progression and excessive delays were common. The route was 2.3 km long with five controlled junctions and three pelican crossings. A low cost traffic management measure of control strategy and revised modelling techniques resulted in annual savings of £143,000 (1986), an abnormal transfer of traffic on to the route (volume increase of approximately 40%), improvement of journey time (approximately 20%), improvement in delayed time (50%), improvement at stops at signals (approximately 60%), improvement in average speed (approximately

25%). The absence of on-street parking in the evening peak has assisted in achieving similar benefits for the evening peak period to those achieved in the morning peak.

Junction improvement - Anniesland Cross

18. This junction is formed by the intersection of two major routes plus a substantial local distributor. The problems were the signal control of the existing junction, the volume of traffic and high proportion of turning movements, pedestrian facilities being justified on all arms of the junction but not accommodated, and traffic re-routing through residential areas to avoid the junction.

19. It was considered that low cost traffic management measures could not be effective, and a complete redesign of the junction was undertaken. Four controlled junctions acting as one were created, the detailed design used being the TRANSYT model. The total cost of the scheme was £2 million with an annual savings of £462,000 (1985), an abnormal increase in traffic volumes (approximately 30%), improvement in journey time (approximately 30%), improvement in delayed time (approximately 50%), improvement in stops at signals (approximately 20%) and improvement in average speed (65%).

20. Congestion at junctions can be accurately assessed, and reduced or eliminated by traffic management schemes, or a combination of traffic management and construction.

Conclusion

20. Congestion can be predicted and cured by civil engineers, by providing the physical infrastructure or management techniques to meet the demands of the public. What cannot be predicted is whether the public or their elected representatives wish for continual infrastructure development to meet the insatiable demands of the motor vehicle. It may be asked whether road congestion should be avoided by increasing road provision, or alternatively vehicles discouraged by measures such as road pricing and cheap alternative forms of transport. To limit road construction so that congestion becomes self-regulating does not seem a sensible policy for a civilized society. Roads must be planned to meet demand, or some roads planned and some other forms of transport provided in parallel to attract demand away from roads. Civil engineers can provide the transport strategies and deal with the implementation - the policy decision must rest with Government.

E12. Northern Ireland Association

1. The population of Northern Ireland is 1,567,000 with a density of 111 persons/km^2. It is expected to increase by 7.3% by the year 2001.

2. As a result of a redevelopment programme there has been a movement of population from Belfast city to the surrounding districts which have recorded population growths ranging from 11-39%. It is only in the Belfast area that any degree of congestion occurs and this is confined to road traffic.

3. The Belfast Transportation Strategy Review (BTSR) which was completed in April 1987 identified certain areas and corridors where congestion is likely to occur by the year 2001. More recent surveys indicate that traffic is increasing more rapidly than was forecast and that congestion will be experienced earlier than was anticipated by the consultants.

4. As a result of the BTSR the DoE has made certain proposals for dealing with the problems which have been identified. These have been the subject of a public inquiry and the inspector's report is awaited.

5. There is a total of 23,730 km of public roads in Northern Ireland of which 110 km are motorways. This represents 70 km of motorway per million of the population. Car ownership is 267 per 1000 population and the number of mechanical vehicles licensed in 1986 was 472,855.

6. Expenditure on major road works has been progressively reduced from £25 million in 1980-81 to £10 million in 1987-88. There has been an increase in funding for maintenance works from £33 million in 1979-80 to £47 million in 1987-88. Total expenditure over the period fell from £70 million to £66 million.

7. The majority of merchandise to and from Northern Ireland is transported by means of containers, either by ro-ro (roll-on roll-off) or lo-lo (lift-on lift-off). Larne Harbour is the second busiest UK port in terms of commercial ro-ro vehicles. Even with the improvements which are currently in progress the A75 which links the Loch Ryan ports of Stranraer and Cairnryan to Carlisle will be inadequate for the traffic which it carries. The A77 from these ports to Ayr carries the bulk of traffic between Scotland and Northern Ireland and is in urgent need of major reconstruction.

Tackling the problem

8. It is essential to draw a distinction between congestion in urban areas and on the inter-urban network. The causes and the possible solutions are different.

Urban areas

9. Congestion in urban areas is caused by large volumes of commuters. With the use of the latest computer technology positive action should be taken to disperse centres of employment away from

96

congested areas by using taxation mechanisms or by the Government taking direct action to move government departments, for example the army from Aldershot. At least one insurance company in the USA operates from the South of Ireland.

10. High capacity limited access roads should be provided to remove heavy goods vehicles from city streets.

11. Adequate car parks should be provided close to major traffic routes and parking controls vigorously enforced in the area.

12. The performance of junctions can be optimized by redesign and efficient traffic management using the latest traffic signalling techniques.

13. In major conurbations road pricing will have to be adopted

Inter-urban network

14. A programme of providing dual carriageways on all trunk roads should be implemented, commencing with relatively short sections so as to allow queues of traffic behind slow moving HGVs to clear.

15. Major road junctions should be grade separated.

16. Lane rentals should be introduced for all statutory undertakers imposing restrictions on the width of carriageways.

Economic considerations

17. Research in Northern Ireland has shown that transport costs on products delivered to the Continent are only a small percentage, say 0.6% of the unit cost of labour intensive products. The cost of congestion on the final cost is therefore insignificant.

18. Action should be taken to improve access to the ports in the North East of England and to develop ro-ro facilities in these ports.

Annex F. Abbreviations

AADF	–	Annual average daily flow
ALA	–	Association of London Authorities
AVI	–	Automatic vehicle identification
BAA	–	British Airports Authority
BR	–	British Rail
BRF	–	British Road Federation
BTSR	–	Belfast Transportation Strategy Review
CBI	–	Confederation of British Industry
CITRAC	–	Centrally integrated traffic control
CSO	–	Central Statistical Office
DoE	–	Department of the Environment
DTi	–	Department of Trade and Industry
DTp	–	Department of Transport
EC	–	European Community
GDP	–	Gross domestic product
GLC	–	Greater London Council
HGV	–	Heavy goods vehicle
IMF	–	International Monetary Fund
LA	–	Local authority
LBA	–	London Boroughs Association
LMTA	–	London Metropolitan transport authority
LRT	–	London Regional Transport
LUL	–	London Underground Limited
MOVA	–	Microprocessor optimized vehicle automation
MTA	–	Metropolitan transport authority
PNR	–	Private non-residential
PTA	–	Passenger Transport Authority
PTE	–	Passenger Transport Executive
RTC	–	Regional transportation committee
SCOOT	–	Split control offset optimization technique
SDD	–	Scottish Development Department

Annex G. Membership

Infrastructure Policy Group

Sir Frank Gibb (Chairman)	Chairman, Taylor Woodrow Group
J. Dromgoole	Director (Council Secretariat), Institution of Civil Engineers
M. J. N. Barnett	Assistant Director, Project Advisory Department, Kleinwort Benson Ltd
Professor A. Budd	Economic Adviser, Barclays Bank plc
P. A. Cox	*formerly* Chairman, Rendel Palmer and Tritton
S. F. Hall	Director of Engineering, Rotherham Metropolitan Borough Council
M. King	Managing Director, Airports Division, BAA
Professor A. D. May	Professor of Transport Studies, Leeds University Consultant to MVA Consultancy
S. N. Mustow	Consultant, W S Atkins
B. Oldridge	Director of Transportation, Cambridge County Council
D. J. Palmer	Confederation of British Industry
Dr T. M. Ridley	Managing Director, Eurotunnel
C. Snowden	City Engineer, Corporation of London
N. A. Soper	*formerly* Assistant Managing Director, Tarmac Construction Ltd

Intra City Group

S. F. Hall (Chairman)	Director of Engineering, Rotherham Metropolitan Borough Council
D. A. Butler	City Engineer, Oxford City Council
P. Gross	City Engineer, Sheffield
W. S. McAlonan	Director of Roads, Strathclyde Regional Council
K. McQueen	Director of Technical Services, London Borough of Wandsworth
S. J. McLeod	City Engineer, Manchester City Council
G. T. Mabb	City Engineer, Cardiff City Council
A. B. Miller	City Engineer, Bristol City Council
B. Raper	City Engineer, Leicester
D. Rawson	City Engineer, Birmingham City Council
J. Tracey	Deputy City Engineer, Manchester City Council
A. Williams	Director of Public Works, London Borough of Southwark

Local association teams

London	C. Snowden S. Miller	G. Alexander P. Simpson	A. Carroll
South Eastern	G. R Holland B. Kermode	M. N. T. Cottell D. Mulrenan	D. Hodgkinson
Southern	Professor P. Morice	I. G. Cross	D. E. Tarrant
Home Counties	G. J. J. Davies D. Jones D. Rattue	J. Hannah C. Nash W. A. J. Sketch	E. Hepper J. Ratliff
East Anglian	R. E. Calvert J. F. Edwards M. A. Roberts	S. Boyle L. Egan G. B. Stead	G. Durham R. J. Randerson
South Wales	F. L. H. Straw Dr G. Pickering	J. G. Evans R. H. Pullan	G. Ll. John
North Western	D. Burnett D. J. Ling L. L. Whyte	T. Deane J. Milne	R. J. Knapman P. F. Reilly
Midlands	N. Heathcote D. Rawson	I. C. Hobbs J. T. Stevenson	T. Mulroy
East Midlands	H. J. Parry	W. Gallear	B. Raper
Yorkshire	R. L. Relph P. Bonsall R. H. King M. J. Smith	R. Ashworth R. Brisbourne R. J. Pickup	R. K. Bird I. D. Jones P. C. Redfern
Northern Counties	W. Pattison	M. Ballinger	W. Donkin
Glasgow and West of Scotland	R. J. C. Stobie	R. McGowan	
Edinburgh and East of Scotland	R. J. C. Stobie	A. H. McGhee	R. McGillivray
Northern Ireland	T. A. Warnock		

Chapter authors

J. Dromgoole O. Simon	P. J. Fells R. S. C. Stewart	R. P. Huxford

Secretariat

Miss C. E. Berry	R. P. Huxford